# Mastering High Performance Multiprocessor Signaling

Electrical design with the
Intel® QuickPath Interconnect

Dave Coleman
Michael Mirmak

Intel
PRESS

ISBN 13: 978-1-934053-16-4

Publisher: Richard Bowles
Managing Editor: Bruce Bartlett
Editor: David J. Clark
Text Design & Composition: STI Certified
Graphic Art: Richard Eberly and Margaret A. Anderson, Ron Bohart (cover))

**Library of Congress Cataloging in Publication Data:**

Printed in China

10 9 8 7 6 5 4 3 2 1

First printing February 2010

**IMPORTANT**

You can access the companion Web site for this book on the Internet at:

**www.intel.com/intelpress/qpied**

Use the serial number located in the upper-right hand corner of the last page to register your book and access additional material, including the Digital Edition of the book.

*In the effort to author my part of this book, I have leaned on family and friends and asked them to be understanding while I have been busy writing. I would like to especially thank my wife Epiphany for her kind patience and cooperation, plus my dog Maggie for keeping me company.*

*—DC*

*The contents of this book, as in any engineering project, are the result of countless hours of work by diligent architects, designers, platform applications engineers and others who worked together to make Intel® QuickPath Interconnect a reality. Their efforts continue in ways that any publication can only vaguely indicate. We simply cannot give them enough credit.*

*As a result, I dedicate this book to the thinkers and doers, from one who merely explains.*

*—MM*

# Contents

## Chapter 4 - Time and Frequency Domain Modeling and Simulation   101

## Chapter 5 - Printed Circuit Board Design Considerations   137

## Chapter 6 - Measurement and Validation   171

# Foreword

From my experience as both a user and a designer of high performance bus interconnect channels, the Intel® QuickPath Interconnect (Intel® QPI) represents a scalable processor interface that provides significant improvements over the performance of the previous generation channel, the Front Side Bus. Intel QPI takes the most critical path for a computing platform's performance from a single-ended source-synchronous approach to the serial-differential channel architecture increasingly common in industry today. Data checking and self-repair remove the effects of many catastrophic errors. The lower voltages and nodal structure of Intel QPI make it applicable and effective for use not only in systems with a single processor socket but also in systems with dozens of processors. For these reasons and many more, engineers will be designing systems based on this bus channel architecture for the foreseeable future.

However, every new channel architecture brings additional engineering challenges. This elegant, low-latency, high-bandwidth bus requires state-of-the-art interconnect engineering to achieve its current and future performance goals. Correct electrical design for high-speed serial-differential systems is not self-evident. It requires knowledge of the relevant transmission line theory, including loss, crosstalk, and reflective effects. Good design also requires an understanding of the basics of driver and receiver analog operation, including equalization. Finally, no interface, particularly a new architecture, can be implemented without defined steps for validation.

Many resources exist on the theory of trace modeling and differential device design. A few are available on PCB design and validation. But designers using a new interface, particularly one with the unique features of Intel QPI, require more. For a PCB designer, any text must cover the basic theoretical concepts and the specifics of the bus, including its pitfalls, in a practical, accessible way. In this book, Dave Coleman and Michael Mirmak do not disappoint. Both Dave and Michael are highly capable engineers with a combined experience in signal integrity engineering that alone dwarfs most in the industry. And I'm happy to say that it was while working for, and being mentored by, Dave Coleman in 1992 at the Intel® Scientific Supercomputer Division, I was originally led to the career path of signal integrity engineering.

With their years of experience conveyed with a clarity of language, they lead the reader through the basics of high performance channel design, modeling, simulation and validation. The book provides a broad technical introduction to the challenges of—and accompanying solutions to—the successful design of platforms employing the Intel QuickPath Interconnect. This is a must-have book for anyone starting out in modern Intel processor-based system design and a springboard to further, more advanced topics in interconnect channel modeling and simulation.

*Scott McMorrow*

# Preface

Today's microprocessor-based computing systems are faster and more capable than anything even dreamed of during the early days of ENIAC or the personal computing revolution of the late 1970s. But system designers, no matter how complex the architecture they use, share a common need to translate high-level structure and concepts into the physical construction and validation methods to make the architecture useful.

The introduction of the Front Side Bus (FSB) in 1994 revolutionized both the performance of microprocessor-based machines but also the way the physical systems were designed. With the FSB, multiple processors could communicate across a structured interconnect, with specific design, signal integrity and validation rules for the physical PCB system implementing it. Now the Intel® QuickPath Architecture emerges as the successor to the FSB, bringing both enormous speed increases but also new considerations and challenges to the system designer. This book is intended to guide the system designer in addressing these, to use the full potential of the Intel® QuickPath Architecture.

The strength of the Intel QuickPath Architecture in the physical or PCB design realm is in both its familiarity and its innovation. It shares many features with other serial-differential interfaces available today, so many of the concepts, such as differential signaling or equalization, may be known to the reader. However, Intel QuickPath has many unique aspects which the platform designer must consider in her or his work. We hope that, with this book, PCB designers will have the confidence to incorporate Intel QuickPath into their systems and reap its many benefits.

## Who Should Read This Book

Most specifications, even when written for the computer industry, unfortunately fail to provide the kind of detail and guidance that a PCB design, signal integrity, or validation engineer would need to actually make the specified thing work. This book was written with the real system engineer in mind, so that he or she can apply simple rules of thumb where they are appropriate, and perform system simulation or lab analysis where they aren't.

A person reading this book who has experience with other high-speed serial-differential interfaces, such as PCI Express[†], will likely find much of it familiar. This is no accident. The concepts behind Intel QPI, PCI Express, and the higher-speed variants of even USB are rapidly becoming ubiquitous. The convergence of computer I/O technology is slowly making eye diagrams, differential signaling, and similar ideas almost universally applicable across platform designs. As a result, this book should have a "ring of truth" to engineers experienced with serial-differential bus design and should provide a relatively relaxed introduction for those who are not. Regrettably, in the world of technology, simply putting the words on a printed page ensures those words are immediately out of date. Simulation and validation tools (and the flows that use them) have to be kept updated, especially as speeds and performance demands increase. We therefore recommend using this book as a starting point, both for your investigation of serial-differential interfaces and of Intel QPI in particular. Use the Web references, mailing lists and other "living documents" we mention, and contact your local Intel representative, to keep your knowledge fresh.

## What's in Store in This Book

We attempt to provide a concept-to-fruition guide to the electrical and physical challenges in planning, designing, and validating an Intel® QPI system. We do not provide specifics on running Intel tools or on debugging individual platform design issues.

You are invited go to this book's companion Web page at www.intel.com/intelpress/qpied for a digital edition of the book, training information and live reference links.

## Chapter Content Guide

Chapter 1 introduces the historical evolution of various platform signaling interfaces, leading up to the development of Intel QPI. After illustrating the efficiency challenges of multiprocessor and memory controller performance, the chapter leads to the improvements provided by Intel QPI, including specific comparisons to PCI Express[†]. The Intel QPI layered architecture is explored as well as some introductory link initialization, training, signal timing, and performance concepts. For those readers interested a detailed discussion of the logical operation of Intel QPI, please refer to the companion book *Weaving High Performance Multiprocessor Fabric: Architectural Insights into the Intel® QuickPath Interconnect*, by Robert A. Maddox, Gurbir Singh, and Robert J. Safranek.

Chapter 2 explores the basis and definitions of the electrical specifications. The motivations for defining common and platform-dependent specifications are rooted in platform performance, interoperability, and validation as well as other cost and reliability considerations. Concepts key to the specifications including differential signaling, unit interval, and jitter are covered in detail and then applied to the transmitter, receiver, and clock specifications.

Chapter 3 presents a basic outline of signal integrity theory. This includes a summary of the parameters that most affect a high-speed interface, such as loss and jitter. The chapter also reviews the basic theory of equalization in transmitters, showing its impact on signals at the receiver inputs.

Chapter 4 reviews how the signal integrity effects outlined in Chapter 3 may be modeled to simulate the behavior in an Intel QPI system. The chapter describes how transmitters, interconnects and receivers can be efficiently represented in both time and frequency domains. The chapter also covers the Intel's recommended analysis tool flow and metrics for evaluating Intel QPI interfaces in simulation.

Chapter 5 describes the rules for actually implementing Intel QPI in a physical printed circuit board. The chapter includes the basic guidelines for trace routing, including serpentines, length matching, and addressing the breakout or escape regions near devices. It also discusses the best practices for adding vias to Intel QPI, as well as mitigating the effects of PCB dielectric fiber weave.

Chapter 6 defines the measurements and equipment needed to validate the Intel QPI specifications. Measurement conditions and reference equipment requirements are outlined for test and board environments. Key validation concepts are applied to specifications that are directly and indirectly measured to verify the Intel QPI transmitter, receiver, clock and interconnect channel performance.

**Note**

The contents of this book are intended only as an overall guide to understanding the PCB design basics of the Intel® QuickPath Architecture. Parties interested in creating either system or component level designs utilizing this technology should contact their local Intel representative for additional information.

The overall Intel® QuickPath Architecture allows for a great deal of implementation flexibility and modular future growth, all within the scope of the architecture. In later sections of this text when we talk of certain characteristics of Intel QPI, we are generally referring to current implementations. Those examples should not be construed as future limitations on the overall scope of the Intel® QuickPath Architecture.

## Authors' Background

**Dave Coleman** is a Staff Platform Applications Engineer at Intel with 22 years of electrical design, modeling and simulation experience. He specializes in enabling and integration of customer Intel® QuickPath Interconnect designs in Intel Server platforms. Dave is the coauthor of the book *PCI Express† Electrical Interconnect Design* published by Intel Press and has contributed articles to Printed Circuit Design magazine. Dave has previously developed platform design guidelines for PCI Express† and InfiniBand† technology platform applications, and served on the PCI Express† Gen1 and Gen2 Cabling workgroups.

**Michael Mirmak** is a Platform Applications Engineer at Intel Corporation. He has been involved with signal integrity modeling and simulation since 1996, developing platform guidelines and models for both processor and chipset products, in desktop, mobile, and server applications. He has been a participant in the IBIS (I/O Buffer Information Specification) Open Forum since 2000 and was the organization's chair from 2003 to 2009.

Michael was a major contributor to the ICM, Touchstone 2.0, and IBIS 4.1–5.0 specifications and also served as the senior editor for the IBIS Modeling Cookbook for Version 4.0. Michael's writing has appeared in the *EE Times* and he has released numerous presentations on technical and standards topics on the Internet. Michael holds a BSEE from the University of Pennsylvania.

## Acknowledgements

A book such as this results from the efforts of more than just the authors named on the cover. An enormous number of people, inside and outside of Intel, contributed time and expertise during the book's development. While we cannot list every individual, we would like to show our appreciation to several teams and groups who helped us make the book a reality.

*For The Technology*

First, we greatly appreciate the vision and ability of the senior technical staff and management of Intel, who turned the concept of Intel® QPI into an integral part of Intel products that will change the industry. They took an enormous risk which is already showing benefits for designers and users worldwide.

Next, we must recognize the individuals in the planning, architecture, design, technical marketing, product marketing, software, validation, and manufacturing teams that put in the many hours of stress and effort to bring real, working products to market. To the Intel® Xeon 5500 processor teams plus the Tukwila, Beckton and other related teams, you have our gratitude and admiration.

*For The Book*

As noted, we cannot name everyone who helped make the book possible. However, several individuals deserve special recognition for their help and encouragement.

The support to write the book from Stephen S. Pawlowski, Intel Senior Fellow and CTO of the Intel Digital Enterprise Group, as well as Intel Press Publisher Richard Bowles, is greatly appreciated.

We deeply appreciate the contributions of Scott McMorrow of Teraspeed Consulting Group LLC for his technical review and comments, and for his Foreword to our book. Thanks also to Ravi Budruk of MindShare for his comments on the text.

Several of our Intel colleagues provided technical content, review comments, and expert answers to our questions. This list includes but is not limited to Shain Bunz, Tom Gondolfi, Paul Gutierrez, Howard Heck, Beomtaek Lee, Robert A. Maddox, and Robert J. Safranek. Many thanks to them for their investment of time and attention.

We are very thankful to the people who took the time to provide the critical validation reviews: Thomas Walley and Peter Meier of Avago Technologies, Aubrey Sparkman of SparkRight Solutions, Sogo Hsu of Foxconn, and Douglas Winterberg of Sun Microsystems.

We would also like to extend our sincere thanks to our management, Gene Pitts, Boyd Davis, Deepti Gupta, and Trevor Williams who supported us in taking the time to write the book.

Our managing editor Bruce Bartlett showed great dedication and patience in the course of many schedule "adjustments" by the authors. Editor David Clark took the language that was perfectly clear to the authors and made it both readable and actually clear to the reader. The clean publication you are holding is the result of the hard work of our production team. We especially recognize the work of Ron Bohart, the designer of our cover art, and Rick Eberly and Margaret Anderson, who took the authors' crude sketches and transformed them into beautiful illustrations.

Thanks to Rich Pangier of Isola Group, SARL, for providing the photographs taken in their R&D laboratory that we used in Figure 3-24. Thanks also to ASSET InterTech, Inc. for providing the Scanworks† IBIST Toolkit figure and photograph in Chapter 6.

For anyone we may have missed, please accept our deepest apologies.

Dave Coleman

Michael Mirmak

November 2009

# Chapter 1

# Intel® QuickPath Interconnect Electrical Architecture Overview

*The art of progress is to preserve order amid change and to preserve change amid order.*

—Alfred North Whitehead

The goal of this chapter is to provide you information to understand the Intel® QuickPath Interconnect (Intel® QPI) architecture basics to establish a context for studying details in the subsequent chapters. This chapter presents some historical background, including other previous and existing architectures leading to the development of Intel QPI. Specific architectural and electrical features are introduced and connected to the Intel QPI electrical specifications.

## Architecture Overview

Intel QuickPath Architecture is designed to provide efficient scalability both logically and electrically. The Intel QuickPath Architecture is a link-based architecture that provides robust point-to-point signaling.

## Historical Context and Motivation

System architecture based on the Front Side Bus (FSB) is a well established design approach for multiple processor systems. As processor and memory architecture have improved and system speed has increased, the FSB has followed suit to maintain a balanced and performing system. This process has continued to succeed for five generations of Intel processors, starting with the Intel® Pentium® Pro and running through the Intel® Pentium 4 processor families.

This shared-bus architecture, continuing the approach of increasing the bus data rates, has reached intrinsic bus challenges for multiple processor systems. Initially configured with five bus loads, 800 million transfers per second (MT/s) was found to be the limiting data rate. Reducing to three bus loads, and then to two, data rates have been pushed to 1333 MT/s. To continue to achieve greater performance, additional FSB interfaces have been added at a cost of 175 signals each, thus requiring memory controllers to become very large devices with more than 1500 pins.

The FSB is designed to provide communication between multiple processors and a single memory controller. Advantages are deterministic in-sequence events, simpler debugging, and observability. However, the FSB brought with it a performance penalty with each added component to the shared bus. With multiple memory controllers in a system, this bus architecture no longer performs adequately. Memory accesses by multiple components in this configuration are already delayed, and with addition of multiple memory controllers, the FSB becomes over-burdened. To compound this, the FSB shares upstream and downstream signaling on individual signals, but supports only unidirectional signaling, not allowing communication simultaneously in both directions. So the FSB either is sending data upstream or downstream on the shared signal wires. Also, the FSB, with 175 signals, is a heavy burden to component pin counts. Lastly, the Gunning Transistor Logic Plus (GTL+) signaling technology is limited to 1.6 gigatransfers per second (GT/s), which limits the interface bandwidth to 12.8 gigabytes per second (GB/s).

The paradigm needs to change in signaling and logical architecture to get to the next level of driving gigabytes per second between components in the printed circuit board (PCB) and improve memory organization and access latencies. Figures 1.1 through 1.3 show comparisons of example shared bus systems which use the FSB, a Memory Controller Hub (MCH) and an I/O Controller Hub (ICH). Figures 1.4 through 1.6 show examples of systems using various Intel QPI signaling configurations that use point-to-point links with distributed memory controllers and I/O Hubs (IOH). These sets of figures show how a shared bus and the Intel QuickPath Architecture are in different performance classes.

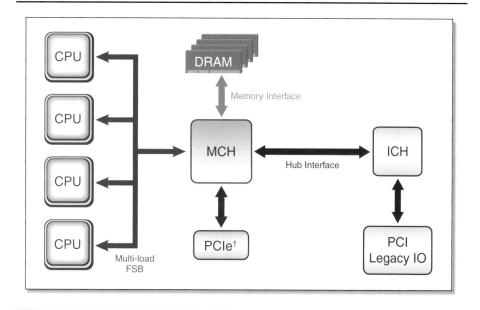

**Figure 1.1**    Four Processor Computer System Based on a Single Front Side Bus

Figure 1.1 shows a system with four processors employing a single shared address and data bus to one chipset component.

- ■ Key advantages
  - – Simpler bus design, analysis, and debug
  - – Global observability among components
  - – Deterministic in-sequence events
- ■ Key disadvantages
  - – Limited bus bandwidth, which goes down with additional components added to the FSB.

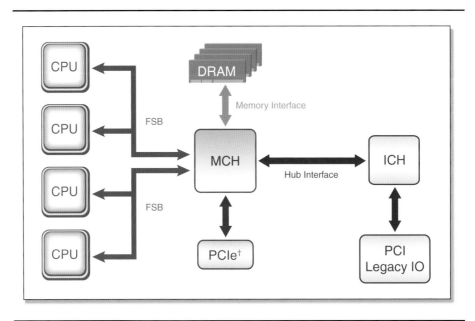

**Figure 1.2**   Four Processor System with Two Front Side System Busses

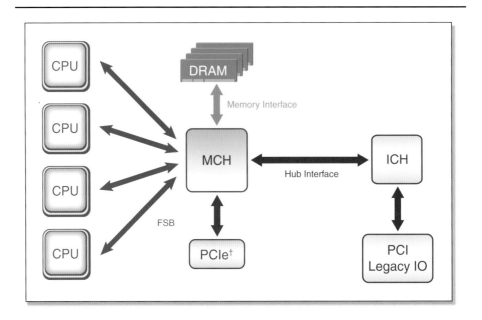

**Figure 1.3**   Four Processor System with Four Independent System Busses

Figure 1.2 shows a system with four processors employing two shared address and data busses with point-to-point links to one shared chipset component. Figure 1.3 shows a system with four processors employing four independent address and data busses with point-to-point links to one shared chipset component.

- ■ Key advantages
  - – Higher bus bandwidth due to point-to-point links
- ■ Key disadvantages
  - – Loss of global observability
  - – Couples system debug with out-of-sequence events
  - – Chipsets become the bottleneck for memory bandwidth

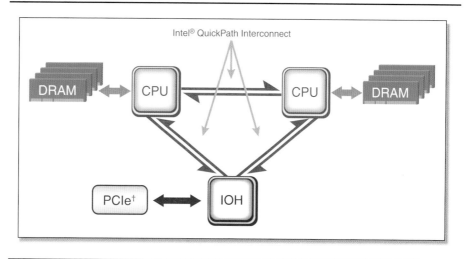

**Figure 1.4**　System with Two Processors Employing Intel® QuickPath Interconnect

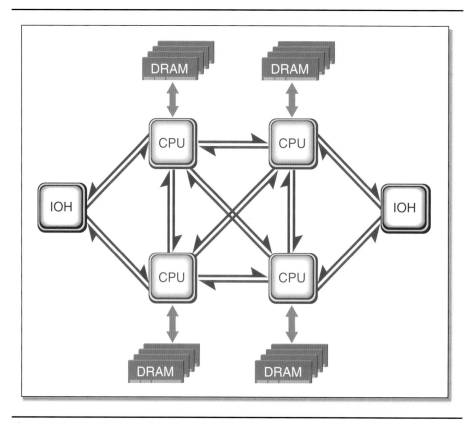

**Figure 1.5**   System with Four Processors Employing Intel® QuickPath Interconnect

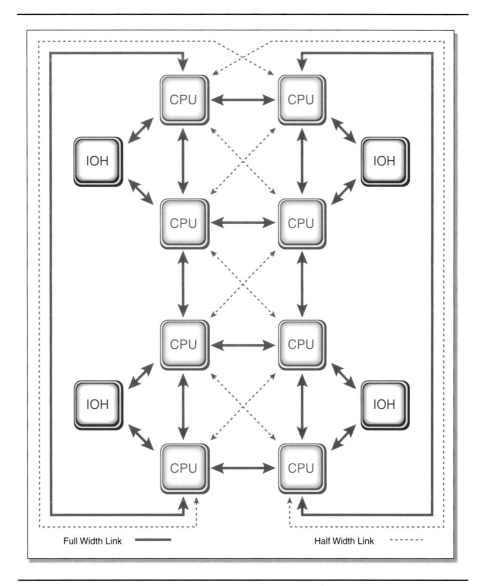

Full Width Link ————  Half Width Link ━ ━ ━ ━

**Figure 1.6** System with Eight Processors Employing Intel® QuickPath Interconnect

Figure 1.4 shows a system with two processors employing Intel QPI links to one chipset component. Figure 1.5 shows a system with four processors employing Intel QPI inks to two chipset components. Figure 1.6 shows a system with eight processors employing Intel QPI links to four chipset components.

These figures show some possible configurations of two-, four-, and eight-processor systems respectively that can be built using the Intel QPI (indicated by the red arrow pairs in the figures). Each processor typically has a memory controller on the same die, allowing systems to be more scalable in performance. However this is not essential and systems can have separate, discrete memory controllers. Similarly, the I/O subsystems can either be incorporated onto the same die as the processors or built as separate I/O hubs.

These systems have multiple Intel QPI links connecting the devices to each other. Each one of the links can operate independently of the other links. The performance of such systems can be very high, particularly if the processors are allocated independent tasks, working on data that are optimally distributed across the different memory controllers and close to their own processors. Most current operating systems do recognize such system configurations with Non-Uniform Memory Accesses (NUMA) from each processor and the OS places the data in the memory accordingly.

■ Key advantages

– Higher bus bandwidth due to point-to-point links

– Efficient memory organization and lower memory access latencies

■ Key disadvantages

– Loss of global observability

– Couples system debug with out-of-sequence events

In Figure 1.6 the memory arrays have been left out and the Intel QPI links are depicted as single lines for clarity. The systems shown in Figures 1.4 through 1.6 are fully connected, at least in that each processor has a direct link to every other processor in the system.

The point-to-point links use fewer signals than the shared bus architecture and provides higher bandwidth, transferring data in both directions simultaneously. The Intel QuickPath Architecture also supports multiple memory controllers and efficiently manages the coherence of the processor caches in the system, which is needed for a multiple processor and scalable server systems. The interface provides a robust set of mechanisms to handle errors and recover from them without shutting down the entire system. Intel QPI is defined to meet these needs.

Serial signaling architectures, such as PCI Express† (PCIe), USB, and SATA take advantage of "packet-based" differential signaling to provide higher signal fidelity and protocol flexibility, and some data reliability as well. Intel QuickPath Architecture is constructed to include these capabilities, as well as additional logical and electrical features, to take advantage of both parallel and serial architectures described later in this chapter.

### Intel® QuickPath Architecture Layer Overview

The Intel QuickPath Architecture is defined to expand the logical and electrical capabilities, as well as to provide flexibility to add to and change the architecture as needed for future requirements. The architecture was also defined to address continuing signaling design and validation challenges. The focus of this book is to address the electrical signaling design, modeling, interconnect implementation, measurement, and validation of Intel QPI. But first, here is an introduction to the overall hierarchy and layer definitions.

The Intel QuickPath Architecture defines different logical layers, with specific functional responsibilities. The Intel QuickPath Architecture layer hierarchy is illustrated in Figure 1.7.

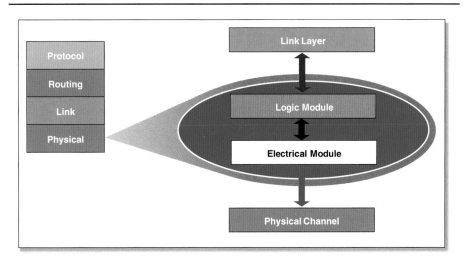

**Figure** 1.7    The Intel® QuickPath Architecture Layer Hierarchy

Intel QPI agents are protocol entities that send/receive a specific type of protocol-level messages. Examples are caching agent, home agent, interrupt agent, etc. Agents are defined at the Protocol layer, and don't have a Physical layer context. There can be multiple agents within a component. The Protocol layer implements the higher level communication protocol between different Intel QPI agents such as cache coherence (reads, writes, invalidations), ordering, peer to peer I/O, and interrupt delivery. The specific functionality of this layer depends on the platform architecture. The Protocol layer may be bypassed in pure routing agents, which results in low latency transfers from sender to receiver through the interconnection network.

The Routing layer provides a flexible and distributed way to route Intel QPI packets from a specific source to a destination based on the destination agent NodeID. It relies on the virtual channel and message class abstraction provided by the Link layer to specify one or more Intel QPI port and virtual network pairs to route the packet. The mechanism for routing is defined through implementation specific routing tables.

The Link layer separates the Physical layer from the upper layers and provides reliable data transfer and flow control between two directly connected Intel QPI agents. The Link layer provides virtualization of the physical channel into multiple virtual channels and message classes. The virtual channels can be viewed as multiple virtual networks for use by the Routing, Transport, and Protocol layers.

The Physical layer logical sub-block interfaces with the Link layer, and reformats the Link layer data flow control units (flits) to be provided to the electrical sub-block. The logical sub-block also re-formats the electrical sub-block physical data units (phits) into flits to transmit to the Link layer. This logical-layer function is transparent to the electrical sub-block and the Link layer, the Link layer not needing to be aware of the electrical sub-block behavior, and vice versa.

The layered architecture provides contextual separation between layers, which also allows a level of independence to changes within each layer, not affecting the other layer definitions. This contextual independence also applies to the Physical layer logical and Electrical sub-blocks.

## Physical Layer Overview

The Physical layer logical and electrical sub-blocks perform separate functions.

The logical sub-block is primarily responsible for Physical layer initialization and training, controlling the electrical sub-block during normal link operation, and Physical layer test and debug hooks. After the Physical layer initialization and training is completed, the logical sub-block works under the direction of the Link layer, which is responsible for flow control. From this link operational point onwards, the logical sub-block communicates with the Link layer at a flit granularity (80 bits) and transfers flits across the link at a phit granularity (20 bits for full-width transfers). A flit is composed of integral number of phits, where a phit is defined as the number of bits transmitted simultaneously in one unit interval (UI) based on the forwarded clock. For instance, a full-width link transmits a complete flit using four phits and receives a complete flit using four phits.

The electrical sub-block defines the electrical signaling technology for high speed data transfer across the link (between agents). Included in the electrical sub-block are the front-end driver and receiver circuits, clock circuitry, analog circuitry for calibrating I/O, detect circuitry, and so on. The electrical sub-block is transparent to the Link layer, and interfaces to the Physical layer logical sub-block.

## Architecture Electrical Features and Definitions

Intel QPI electrical signaling establishes significant changes to FSB, which are useful to compare and contrast with PCIe. There are some key similarities, as well as differences in the link and signaling architecture.

### Link and Port Definitions

Components with Intel QPI ports communicate using a pair of uni-directional point-to-point links, defined as a link pair. Figure 1.8 illustrates four Intel QPI ports, with the top port expanded to show the individual link elements. Each port comprises a Transmit (Tx) link interface and a Receive (Rx) link interface. For the illustrated example, component A has a Port A that is connected to component B Port B. One uni-directional link transmits from Port A to

Port B, and the other link transmits from Port B to Port A. Please note that this port naming is not dictated by Intel QPI and is only being used to illustrate the Intel QPI link connection between two agents. Also, a "transmit" link and "receive" link is defined with respect to a specific agent or port. For Port A, the Port A transmit link transmits data from Port A to Port B. This same Port A transmit link is the Port B receive link.

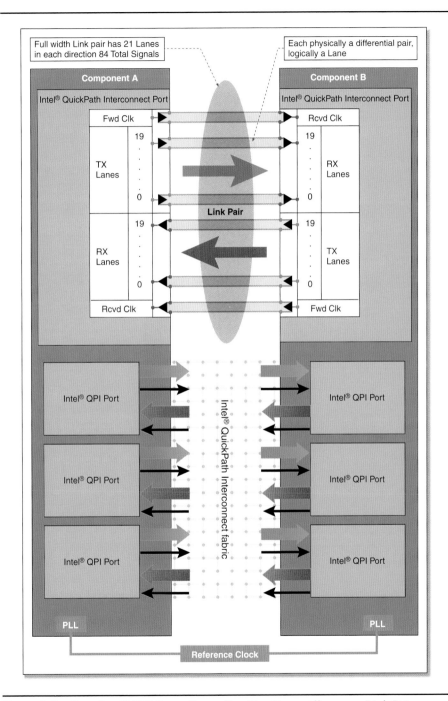

**Figure 1.8**　Four Intel® QPI Ports, Expanding One Port to Illustrate a Link Pair

It is important to note that the link term definition is different than that for PCIe. For PCIe, the pair of Transmit and Receive links is defined as a link, not link pair. One reason that this distinction is made is to provide the Intel QPI link capability to independently change one of the link widths. For example, as shown in Figure 1.9, the Port A Transmit link is a half-width link, while the Port A Receive link is a full-width link. With PCIe, both uni-directional links must remain the same width. There are other logical capabilities that take advantage of this link width independence that are not covered in this book (please refer to the book *Weaving High Performance Multiprocessor Fabric: Architectural insights into the Intel® QuickPath Interconnect Maddox et al., Intel Press 2009* for more information on this).

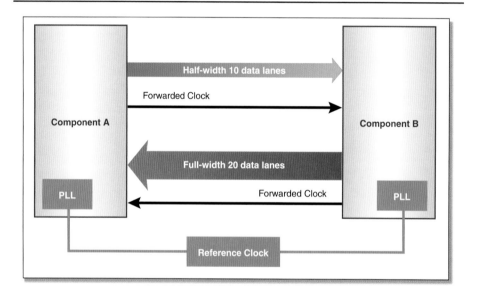

**Figure 1.9**    Two Different Width Intel® QuickPath Interconnect Links

## Signaling and Clocking Definitions

Intel QPI ports have two kinds of signals: data and clock. There are no other side-band signals such as interrupts or control signals, simply data and clock signals. The data and clock signals contain the interrupt and control via the packet definitions.

The data and clock signals are DC-coupled between the link ports, not AC-coupled like PCIe. Since the clock is a separate signal, and is not recovered from the data signals, there is no data encoding (PCIe has 8b/10b encoding). The transmitter (Tx) and receiver (Rx) terminations are also ground referenced. Since many readers are familiar with PCIe, a comparison of Intel QPI and PCIe signaling is listed in Table 1.1.

**Table 1.1**   Intel® QuickPath Interconnect versus PCI Express Electricals

| Definition | Intel QPI | PCI Express† |
|---|---|---|
| Port coupling | DC | AC |
| Clocking | Mesochronous | ppm spec |
| Clock recovery | Forwarded clk | Recovered clk |
| Encoding | None | 8b/10b |
| Signal routing | Differential | Differential |
| Tx equalization | Multi-tap Eq | De-emphasis |
| Rx equalization | Supported, not required | No |
| SSC* | Yes | Yes |

*Spread-spectrum clocking (down-spreading)

All signal lanes are electrically differential. Each lane has two signals (one positive and one negative sense, treated as equal and opposite signals). The "difference" in the positive (D+) and negative (D-) signals of each signal differential pair constitutes the signal amplitude. Figure 1.10 illustrates the signaling definition. Since the data and clock signals are differential, and use the same buffer design, the skew and jitter can be better optimized for higher speed performance. Also, differential signals can be designed to be less susceptible to crosstalk and have lower electromagnetic emissions.

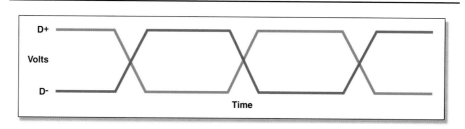

**Figure 1.10**   Differential Signals

Each link has one clock lane, which is called a *forwarded clock*. The forwarded clock is a point-to-point signal sent by the transmitting port to the receiving port. This forwarded clock provides a common timing reference between the transmitting and receiving port Physical layers at each end of the link, as shown in Figures 1.8 and 1.9. So each link has a dedicated forwarded clock, which is phase independent, but has the same clock frequency with respect to other link forwarded clocks.

The forwarded clocks for both links of each link pair are derived from a reference clock, which needs to be at the same frequency (not a part-per-million, or ppm, allowance specification like PCIe) but may have a different phase (that is, the clock edge placement may be different between different clock inputs). The clocks are technically defined as *mesochronous* (same frequency, fixed but independent phase). The important thing is the make sure one clock doesn't drift in frequency compared to the other so that the Physical layer drift buffers may stay within a fixed minimum/maximum drift range.

The forwarded clock lane signal is transmitted at a frequency of half of the data lane data rate. For example, if the data lanes are transmitting at 6.4 gigabits per second (also denoted Gb/s or equivalently, GT/s for gigatransfers per second), the forwarded clock frequency is 3.2 gigahertz (GHz). Both the clock rising and falling edges are used to latch the data, thus at a rate of 2x the clock frequency, 6.4 Gb/s.

The forwarded clock lane is not directly utilized to latch the data for each data lane. Instead, the forwarded clock provides a clock copy, which is distributed to each receiving lane circuit, each of which has its own phase interpolator (PI). Each lane's PI has its placement optimized during bit-lock training, so that each lane "adjusts" the data timing to center the received signal. Figure 1.11 illustrates the individual receiver lane PI setup. This independent lane PI training and placement allows lane-to-lane routing flexibility on the PCB.

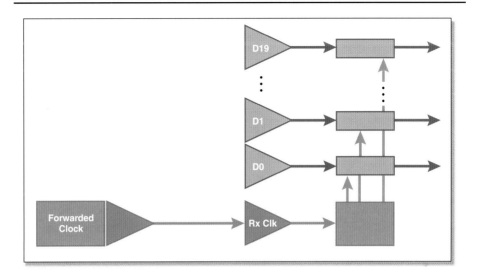

**Figure 1.11** Individual Lane Clocks

To optimize signaling for different interconnect lengths and topologies, Intel QPI has advanced the transmitter signal conditioning. Transmitter equalization is supported and is a multi-tap equalization, compared to PCIe with a single-stage de-emphasis. For Tx equalization, multi-tap equalization is defined to provide pre-cursor, cursor, and post-cursor amplitude conditioning. PCIe, in comparison, employs a single post-cursor de-emphasis. Intel QPI and PCIe Tx equalization schemes are contrasted in Figure 1.12.

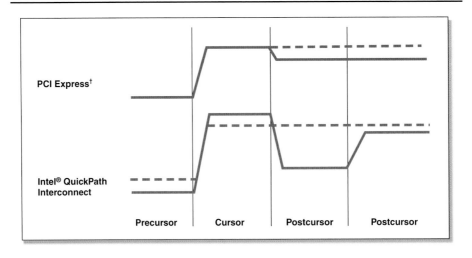

**Figure 1.12** Transmitter Equalization Schemes

## Basis of Timing and Signal Quality Budgeting

The signals transmitted between Intel QPI ports need to be effectively recognized as a logical "0" or "1" at the receiving port. The signal construct is defined by the voltage amplitude (height) and time (width) "envelope" which is called an eye. As seen in Figure 1.13, it is evident why the term *eye* readily applies. Due to the interconnect losses and sources of signal interference (such as crosstalk, reflections) the eye size and quality degrades as it travels to the receiver. Signals with longer trace lengths and connectors will experience more signal degradation. Figure 1.13 illustrates a typical eye at the transmitter and receiver of a sample lane.

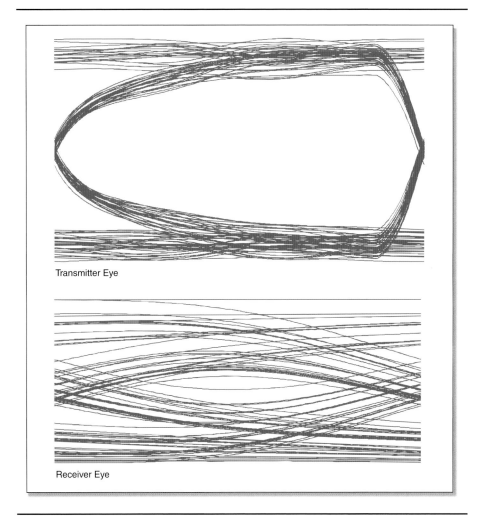

Transmitter Eye

Receiver Eye

**Figure 1.13** Transmitter and Receiver Eyes

Both the eye width and height need to be of adequate size at the receiver for the receiver to recognize a logical "0" or "1". If not, then the receiver may erroneously detect the signal as the opposite logic value. This detection error is called a *bit error*. The measure of the bit errors that occur during a number of bits transmitted is called the *bit error rate*, also known as the BER. BER is the ultimate measure of link electrical performance, and is specified in the Intel QPI electrical specification. The BER is also one of the "common" specifications, which means that the value of BER is the same across all Intel QPI product implementations. For all implementations, the allowed BER is $1 \times 10^{-14}$ per lane, which means that only up to 1 bit error in $10^{14}$ bits transmitted is allowed.

For signal timing and voltage budgeting, the eye is one of the criteria used to determine signal performance "goodness." The BER is the indirect validation target of receiver performance "goodness." Since the receiver input is not accessible by probing hardware, the receiver performance needs to be validated indirectly by use of the BER measurement.

The interconnect loss and interference effects on the eye have been discussed, but a couple of other sources of signal quality impact need to be budgeted as well—jitter, and duty cycle distortion. Jitter is the variation of one or more signal edges away from the fundamental (ideal) signal frequency or period. Figure 1.14 illustrates the concept of signal jitter. For example, an ideal clock signal will have a duration, or period of 1/frequency. Jitter is the deviation from that period between a rising edge and another rising edge (or between falling edges). Duty cycle distortion is another high versus low signal variation that distorts the signal voltage and timing. Jitter and duty cycle distortion are discussed conceptually in more detail in Chapter 2 and Chapters 3 and 4 for modeling and simulation considerations.

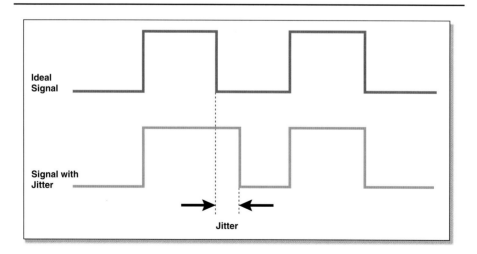

**Figure 1.14** Signal Jitter

A simple way to view the timing impact on the signal due to jitter and duty cycle distortion is to note that if the signal rising or falling edge placement changes, the phase interpolator of the receiver (previously trained to "look" at a specific time) will not be optimally placed if the signal rising or falling edges are "jumping" around.

## Other Signaling Requirements

Intel QPI is designed to accommodate a wide range of platform types and interconnect topologies. Specific common requirements are defined for BER, clocking, termination, DC coupling, spread-spectrum clocking (SSC) and electrostatic discharge protection (ESD). These requirements are also critical to provide interoperability and compatibility, which are discussed in Chapter 2.

The reference clock needs to be common to all Intel QPI components that have interconnected ports. The reference clock frequency needs to be fixed (not a ppm specification as for PCIe), but the phase, or timing of the clock edges from one receiving component to another is not critical. The clock phase relationship between components is not important, but the jitter is important, which is discussed in later chapters. Each component that receives the reference clock will be converting (and multiplying) the clock frequency with its own phase locked loop (PLL), so the phase is lost in the mix.

What is important is the "drift" of the reference clock. The drift is the longer term variation of the clock phase (for example, the clock edge delaying and/or moving in over time compared to the ideal clock frequency). The clock drift specifications are discussed in more detail in Chapter 2.

Intel QPI requires specific Tx and Rx termination during the link initialization, training, and active operation. These termination definitions are common across all platform implementations. Specifically, three impedance ranges are defined: Open (high impedance), detect (specific range between high and low impedance), and low (active, operational and compliance impedance of lower value). These specific termination cases are common across all platform configurations.

Since Intel QPI is DC-coupled between each port transmitter and receiver, all of the interconnect components need to effectively conduct electrical signals, or equivalently, power at specific high data rates. So the transmitter and receiver package, socket, connector or any other element that is part of the interconnect topology, needs to provide an electrical DC path to each other element. Cables are not explicitly covered in the specifications, but can be utilized as long as the performance requirements are satisfied.

Intel QPI supports a common standard ESD model, to protect the component circuits. The protection level is specified, but the implementation is not restricted to a specific circuit design. This allows the individual designer to use a circuit that is optimized to the component process and circuit library.

Spread-spectrum clocking (SSC) is supported for all implementations. SSC is defined as a "down-spreading" of the reference clock frequency, to vary between the operating frequency, and 30 KHz below the operating frequency. This allows the EMI envelope to have reduced frequency power peaks by spreading the frequency.

## Link Initialization and Training

The link initialization and training is covered in more detail in *Weaving High Performance Multiprocessor Fabric,* but is introduced here to point out some of the key electrical dependencies. The initialization and training steps are described in the actual sequence, which is shown in Figure 1.15.

In order to optimize the data signal transfer timing (and at a logical level, pattern recognition to construct, transmit, and deconstruct the packet information), the link needs to detect signals on each lane, and deskew signals between the lanes within a link. The training also identifies and corrects electrical signal polarity and logical lane reversal. All of this is done for the Physical layer transmit and receive data integrity. The higher Intel QPI layers are abstracted from this level of signal attention.

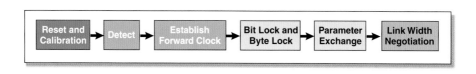

**Figure 1.15** Link Initialization and Training

*Reset/Calibrate*

This is the initial state from which the link emerges to initialize and train. During this state, the PLL locks onto the reference clock and internal circuit calibration may be done prior to entering the detect state.

*Detect*

Once reset is completed, Detect.clkterm is initiated. This is the first initialization state, in which the link transmitter actively checks for clock termination at the receiver. All other data signals are in the open (high-impedance) state at this time. Once the clock termination is detected, the Detect.FwdClock state is initiated.

*Establish Forwarded Clock*

In Detect.FwdClock the port forwarded clock transmitter starts sending a clock signal. Simultaneously, the transmitter data signals also activate their detect circuitry. Once the receiver locks onto the clock signal, the receiver data signal pull-down terminations are activated. The DC pattern state is entered once the receiver data lane terminations are detected.

The next state is Detect.DCPattern. The port data transmitters drive a differential DC logical "1" on all data lanes so that the receiver can check the signal state. At this time, polarity inversion is checked and corrected.

*Polling.BitLock*

At this stage, each receiver data lane trains the PI to be placed to adequately latch valid data. Ideally, the PI will be centered in the signal with respect to voltage and time. Intel QPI is designed for high-speed signaling by utilizing a PI for each lane. This allows flexibility to routing and Transmitter data lane output skew, which at higher frequencies may amount to multiple data symbols.

*Polling.ByteLock, Polling.LaneDeskew, and L0*

Once the BitLock is completed, the training is past the analog part of the training and into the logical training. ByteLock is used to identify the byte (8-bit) boundary so that the lanes can be logically deskewed (on a bit-scale, or unit interval, UI incremental basis).

As far as the link training is concerned, after the deskew process come the steps to establish lane ID, linkwidth, and other configuration parameters prior to entering the active signaling state, L0. Once these hand-shake steps are completed, L0, the active transaction state, is entered.

## Technology and Interoperability

Besides high-speed signaling operation, Intel QPI is designed to encompass a wide range of process technologies and platform applications. It is intended to support components of different process technologies connected via Intel QPI ports. Intel QPI also allows individual components, such as processors, chipsets, node controllers, and others to interoperate in multiple platform segments or applications.

One of the goals of defining common specifications is to ease of some of the burdens of interoperability. The common BER rate and termination cases are examples of this. Another advantage of defining the common specifications is simplification of validation procedures and measurement techniques.

# Chapter 2

# Electrical Specification Overview

The primary electrical signaling goal is to exchange correct data between transmitting and receiving components within acceptable margins to ensure an adequate signal bit error rate by the receiver. To do this, the signal needs to meet the clock, transmitter, and receiver signal timing and quality requirements. Also, the signal performance targets need to be the same for simulation, electrical design, and validation tasks. The desire is to connect the electrical simulation, layout, validation, and test/measurement to share a common context, so that the simulation performance and validation measurement are the same.

## The Specification Approach

The Intel® QuickPath architecture applies to Intel platforms ranging from high-end scalable systems to single processor platforms. It applies to both the Intel® Xeon® processor family (XPF) and Intel® Itanium® processor family (IPF) components. In order to apply this architecture to the wide range of platforms and components, architectural decisions have been made to define some common (shared) requirements and platform-specific specifications.

The tradeoffs among interoperability, performance, manufacturing costs, and validation methods form the basis of the electrical specifications. What is common across all components and platforms versus what is defined for individual platforms provides an overall result of an interconnect system architecture that allows design and manufacturing flexibility, achieves high-speed performance and common electrical validation methods.

Interoperability is the ability for more than one set of components to work together in a system design. One aim of defining the common specifications is to allow Intel components to interoperate with other Intel components with different processes (for example, 90nm and 45nm), or Intel components with external silicon developer components, such as node controllers.

For example, an IO Hub component (IOH) may be designed to interoperate electrically with different processor products or platform types as shown in Figure 2.1. In order to do this, the IO Hub component must be electrically compatible with all of the different processor component electrical specifications, as well as the platform Intel QPI link topologies.

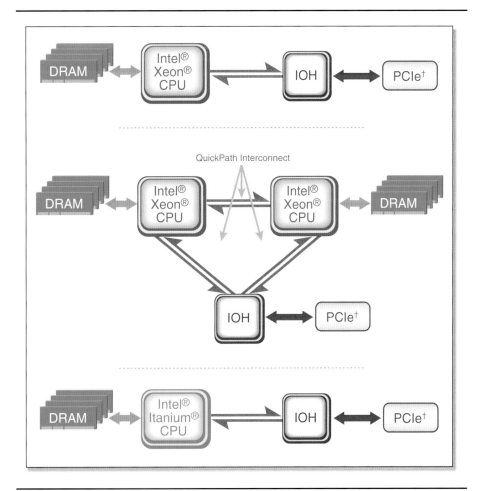

**Figure 2.1**  Intel® QPI Interoperability

Interoperability among Intel QPI components is essential to ensure that each component physical layer works with a selected set of other components without requiring unique characteristics for each link pair. Interoperability definitions also provide a common infrastructure to allow test and debug equipment such as oscilloscopes, logic analyzers, and automated test equipment (ATE) to properly and consistently operate.

Interoperability provides a level of flexibility for platform designs, but does have limits. One of the drawbacks of a "general" electrical specification would be that the signaling performance would be compromised if interoperability were needed across all platforms and all components. The signal voltage and timing margins, being affected by different platform topologies and routed lengths, would for example need to meet a two-connector topology as well as a topology with no connectors. Clearly, to meet the more demanding two-connector topology, the signals would have much more margin in the no-connector topology, but the no-connector topology performance would be limited by the constraint to be interoperable with the two-connector topology.

For this reason, to allow better performance optimization for different topologies, topology classes have been defined to provide interoperability within classes, without requiring interoperability across all classes. In fact, to allow some level of interoperability across topology classes, Intel® QPI interoperability provides the capability to allow more severe topologies (for instance, two-connector physical channels) to interoperate with less severe topologies (one or no connector).

This is a one-way interoperability definition. The physical layer (PHY) designed to meet the two-connector topology (PHY1) may interoperate with a one connector (PHY2) and a no-connector PHY topology (PHY3). However, the PHY designed to meet the PHY3 topology may not interoperate with the PHY2 or PHY1 topology. This is an interoperation hierarchy as shown in Figure 2.2.

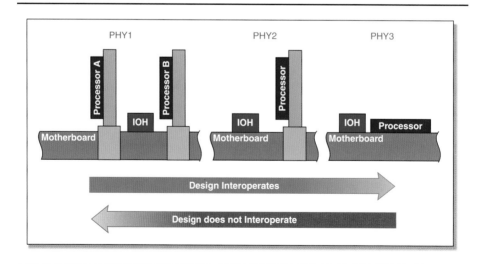

**Figure 2.2** PHY1, PHY2 and PHY3 Interoperability

The PHY1 topology is the most severe of the three topology types. It is targeted for 4-socket (and higher socket count) server platforms, also known as enterprise multi-socket or mission critical class servers. The PHY2 topology generally targeted for a dual-socket server class platform and the PHY3 topology is for the uni-socket server or desktop class platform. A component designed to operate in a PHY1 topology will be able to operate in the less severe PHY2 and PHY3 topologies, hence the interoperability with the PHY2 and PHY3 topologies. In fact a platform with components that are PHY1 compatible may include PHY2 or PHY3 topologies in the platform.

Another aim of the common specifications is to provide flexibility for a component to operate in multiple socket platform cases. For example, a component may operate in both a 4-socket and 2-socket platform. The general rule to support this capability is that the 4-socket capable component may work in the 2-socket platform. However, a component designed for a 2-socket platform may not as easily operate in a 4-socket platform.

Generally, similar to the 2-connector through no-connector topology case, a 4-socket platform topology is more challenging than a 2-socket topology. Similarly, a 2-socket topology is more demanding than a 1-socket topology. This is due to multiple factors, including interconnect lengths and may extend to the number of connectors needed.

The Intel® QPI specifications include both common and differentiated specifications. The common specifications provide platform flexibility and help facilitate interoperability and validation. Optimized performance, however, is still needed for individual platform cases that stress the link transfer rates (4.8 GT/s, 6.4 GT/s, and so on), and the interconnect topology trace lengths and use of connectors.

Another tradeoff of having a "general" interoperable specification would be that the requirements could constrain products to be designed to overperform given what is necessary for the topology requirements. The overperformance burden would potentially be at the expense of cost or power, for example, either of which could compromise the implementation viability for a particular product market.

Since these constraints impact cost, power, real estate, or other design parameters, Intel QPI has chosen a selective interoperable principle, as opposed to a general interoperable specification. The interoperability criteria are applied to products within a given platform type such as large-scale servers.

To help accomplish the selective interoperability, the Intel QPI electrical parameters have been divided into common parameters and platform-specific parameters. Such a methodology was deemed optimal to satisfy interoperability requirements for platforms without forcing all products to be designed in ways not ideal for their platforms.

Specifications for a higher-speed product within a platform type have been made such that it can be made backward-compatible with a product falling within the same platform and same configuration operating at a lower speed. The signaling circuitry of the higher-speed product must therefore be made compatible with the lower-speed product, should this be a requirement from the platform perspective.

## Interconnect Topologies and Components

Intel QPI supports a range of component interconnect topologies. Included are cases all the way from a single processor socket with no connector to 4-processor socket and above with 2-connector topologies.

Topologies are defined between processors, IO hub, Node Controller, Bridge and other component types. The interconnect topologies are all DC-coupled electrically connected connections, including multilayer printed circuit boards, component packages, sockets, connectors, and interposers. The topology variations include the printed circuit board length/via/breakout/layer implementations, number of connectors and sockets, and number of components connected within a reference clock domain. These interconnect components are discussed in more detail in Chapter 5.

Intel QPI has three classes of signals: data, forwarded clock, and system reference clock. The data and forwarded clock signals comprise the Transmit and Received links of each Intel QPI link pair. The system reference clock is provided to all Intel components that are connected via Intel QPI links, as shown in Figure 2.3.

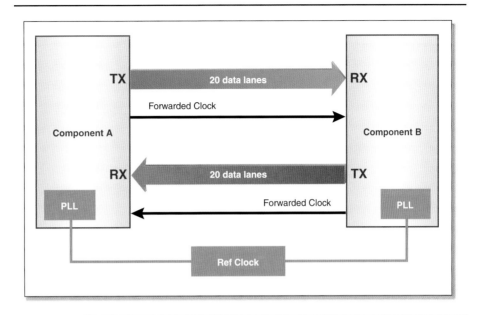

**Figure 2.3**    Intel® QPI Signals

The Intel QPI forwarded clock is a dedicated clock signal in each link. In this forwarded clock scheme, an explicit clock channel is allocated for a clock pattern to be transmitted from one communicating port to the other. One differential clock channel is used for each direction, Tx and Rx, so that any two communicating ports of a link pair have two forwarded clock channels between them.

The system reference clock provides a common clock frequency to all Intel QPI components that are connected via Intel QPI links. This ensures that all of the transmitters and receivers at each end of the link have a common reference clock frequency, as illustrated in Figure 2.4. The reference clock signals are provided as differential signals by a single reference clock source. However additional buffering is allowed between the reference clock and the component inputs, to include all needed components in the clock domain. Each line of the differential output must be terminated with a 50-ohm on-board termination, after the last driver buffer. See the appropriate Intel platform design guide for specific reference clock requirements and implementation suggestions.

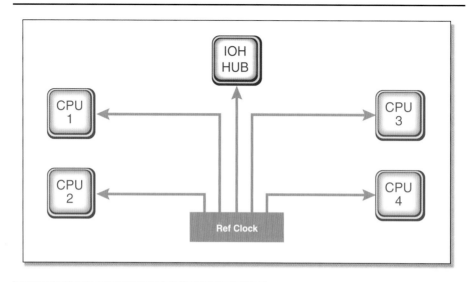

**Figure 2.4**   System Reference Clock

## Essential Electrical Specification Concepts

The ultimate requirement of a digital system electrical design is to meet the data transmission bit error rate (BER) at the link receiver. Some system designs may require perfect bit transmission, but Intel QuickPath architecture is more tolerant, allowing a level of bit errors by specifying a BER per signal lane.

To meet the BER, one needs to design to meet a number of electrical specifications for the transmitter, receiver, clocks, and interconnect channel. Some basic concepts defined and applied to the specifications need to be understood before learning about the specifications. These concepts include signaling type (differential), Unit Interval (UI), signal eye, signal eye mask, jitter, and AC/DC common mode voltage.

### Differential Signaling

Printed circuit boards have two basic types of electrical signaling: single-ended and differential. A single-ended signal is explicitly referenced to a ground signal. A differential signal is defined as a signal pair with a voltage difference between providing a *differential voltage* between the two signal conductors. The convention used here is that the differential signal pair is comprised of a positive conductor, $V_{D+}$, and a negative conductor, $V_{D-}$, to indicate the two signals of a differential pair.

In multilayer signal design, the ideal concept of "differential" is not practical since the signal layers, whether microstrip or stripline, have ground and power planes nearby that partially couple to the signal traces. To cause the signals to behave as differential signals, they are designed to couple more strongly between the differential signal pair than the reference planes and to be symmetrically routed with respect to the planes. This is discussed in more detail in Chapters 4 and 5.

The differential voltage ($V_{DIFF}$) is defined as the difference between the positive conductor and negative conductor voltages:

$$(V_{DIFF} = V_{D+} - V_{D-})$$

The common mode voltage (VCM) is the average, or mean, voltage on the same differential pair:

$$(V_{CM} = [V_{D+} + V_{D-}] / 2)$$

The Intel QPI electrical specifications often utilize the peak-to-peak measurements for validation criteria, as shown in Figure 2.5. The peak-to-peak differential voltages for $V_{D+}$ and $V_{D-}$ can be defined for either symmetric or asymmetric voltage swings, by the following equations for symmetric voltage swing:

$$V_{DIFFp-p} = \quad (2^* \max |V_{D+} - V_{D-}|)$$

and for asymmetric voltage swing:

$$V_{DIFFp-p} = \quad (\max |V_{D+} - V_{D-}| \, \{V_{D+} > V_{D-}\} + \max |V_{D+} - V_{D-}| \, \{V_{D+} < V_{D-}\})$$

The $V_{DIFFp-p}$ is computed for each "eye" or unit interval (UI), both of which are defined in the next section. Since the worst-case $V_{DIFFp-p}$ is the smallest or minimum value, this specification selects the minimum value measured across all of the voltage values measured.

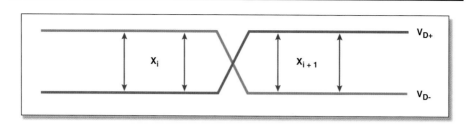

Figure 2.5    Differential Voltage Swing

## Unit Interval (UI), Signal Eye, and Eye Mask

Each Intel QPI link is unidirectional and point-to-point. The Transmitter (Tx) of one component sends a signal to the end of the point-to-point link to the Receiver (Rx) of the other component. Each lane of the link is a differential signal with a binary logic sense (1 and 0).

For this binary signaling, a data bit is sent for each edge of the forwarded clock, whether it is a rising or falling edge. The clock differential signal edge crossing points, from one crossing to the next, define the period of time for each binary data signal transferred. This unit of time is called a unit interval, or UI. The clock signal, since it is a repeating periodic pattern (101010…) is best suited to illustrate the UI concept. The UI convention used for Intel QPI is shown in Figure 2.6, simplified as a single-edge signal to illustrate the rise and fall edges. The first UI in a measured sequence (U1) is the period between a clock edge at time t0 and the next clock edge at t1. The second UI (U2) is the period between t1 and t2, and so on.

The ideal UI is assumed to be based on a steady-state clock with no signal distortion. The UI duration is then one half of the ideal clock cycle period, since the clock cycle includes both the rising edge and falling edge intervals.

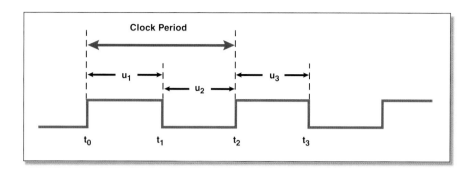

**Figure 2.6** Unit Interval (UI)

In general, the UI for any interval is denoted $UI_n$ for an interval ending in edge n, where each $UI_n$ is defined by

$UI_n = t_n - t_{n-1}$

where $t_n$ and $t_{n-1}$ are consecutive clock or data signal edges, as shown in Figure 2.7. Similarly, multiple consecutive UI are defined by

$xUI = t_n - t_{n-x}$

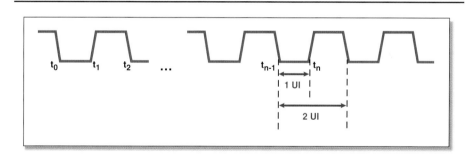

**Figure 2.7** Multiple UI

So, for example, for the signal duration ending at time $t_n$, two UI would be from $t_{n-2}$ to $t_n$.

The clock or data signal that is measured in simulations or validation measurements for differential signals is most often shown with the differential signals superimposed, which is called a signal *eye*. For a single ideal UI eye, it may appear as a hexagon, but when multiple UI signals are superimposed upon each other for non-ideal signals, the appearance is much more like the common oval eye shape of a person or animal.

The eye of the transmitter is a larger voltage amplitude since it has just exited the transmitter output. The eye at the receiver end of the point-to-point channel is often smaller amplitude, due to channel loss and other sources of signal distortion. These eyes are depicted in Figure 1.8 in Chapter 1, but also again here in Figure 2.8.

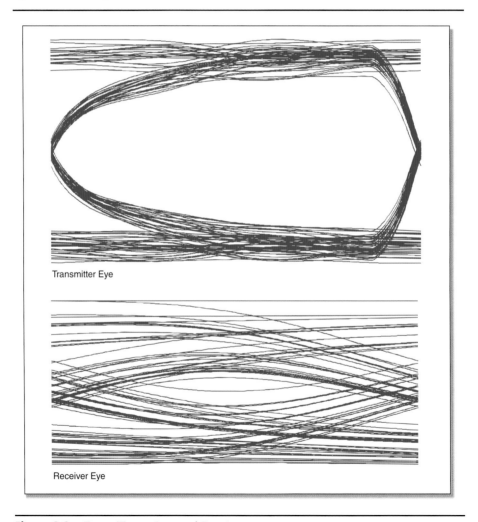

Transmitter Eye

Receiver Eye

**Figure 2.8**   Eye at Transmitter and Receiver

The receiver data signal amplitude and duration are not measured at the receiver pin, but at the receiver input pad. Signals may be observed at the receiver pin, but the amplitude and duration may be significantly different than at the pad. For this reason, the receiver eye mask is not specified, but instead the voltage and time duration margins are specified at the pad. The receiver sensitivity to voltage and timing is validated by margining the receiver, which is discussed in Chapter 6.

## Signal Jitter and Duty Cycle Distortion

We have discussed the unit interval, but only in terms of the ideal unit interval (based on a repeating clock pattern). Due to many different sources of noise, differences in circuit rising and falling edge behavior, signal coupling and reflections, and other effects, the UI may be larger or smaller. The jitter may be random or with some kind of patterned behavior also called deterministic jitter. It may vary from UI to UI, or over a series of UI. If based on driver or receiver asymmetry, it is treated as duty cycle distortion. We will explore each of these effects.

### UI JITTER

The simplest measurement of signal jitter is based on the difference between any given UI and an ideal UI interval. If a number of UI edges are simulated or measured at the edge crossing times $t_1$, $t_2$, …, $t_{n-1}$, $t_n$, $t_{n+1}$,…, $t_K$, where K is the number of samples collected, then the UI jitter for any specific instance of n is defined as:

$$UI(jit)_n = (t_n - t_{n-1}) - T, \quad n = 2,3,...,K$$

where T is the ideal UI size. For a large sample of UI, with random jitter (for example, Gaussian-like jitter: very close to symmetric distribution) the average of the UI sizes approaches the ideal UI size.

Each UI corresponds to one signal digital bit, and two consecutive UI is equivalent to one full cycle, or period of the forwarded clock. For the ideal UI, for 6.4 GT/s signaling, the forwarded clock frequency is 3.2 GHz, with one UI equal to 156.25 picoseconds.

The deterministic jitter and random jitter are analyzed on a different basis. Deterministic jitter has specific frequency components present and is analyzed in terms of the peak-to-peak value, with focus on isolating the causes or sources of the frequency components. Random jitter is typically unbounded so it is analyzed in terms of statistical distributions, and to convert to a bit error rate for the link.

### UI-UI JITTER

UI-UI jitter is different from UI jitter. Whereas UI jitter is the jitter difference between each $UI_n$ and an ideal UI, UI-UI jitter (read as "UI to UI") is defined to be the jitter between any two consecutive UI as shown by

$$\Delta UI_n = UI_n - UI_{n-1} \quad n = 1,2,3,...K$$

### N-UI JITTER

N-UI jitter is a measure of the accumulated jitter over N consecutive UI. The number of consecutive UI, N, is dependent upon the system components and configuration. For a larger MP platform, N may be a range of 5–12 UI, whereas for a DP system, N may be a smaller number in the range of 3–7 for example. The number of UI depends upon several things, including the range of skew between the forwarded clock and data signals, the level of random jitter, power supply noise, and duty cycle distortion. The N-UI accumulated jitter is defined as

$$T_{acc}^{N} = \sum_{p=m}^{m+N} \left( UI_p - \overline{UI} \right) \quad m = 1,2,....,K - N$$

where $\overline{UI}$ is defined as

$$\overline{UI} = \frac{\sum_{p=1}^{K} UI_p}{K} \quad p = 1,2,...,N,...,K$$

K is the total number of UI samples taken, and N is the subset of UI for the N-UI measurement. As shown in Figure 2.9, the N-UI jitter is a measure of the accumulated jitter of the N-UI as compared to a stream of N consecutive ideal UI. The specific validation requirements are outlined in Chapter 6.

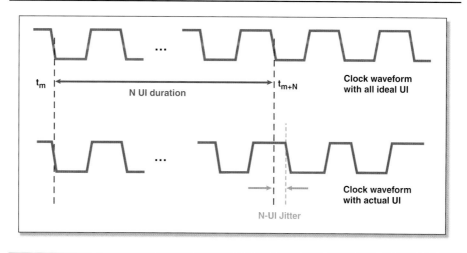

**Figure 2.9** N-UI Jitter

## DUTY CYCLE DISTORTION (DCD)

Duty cycle distortion occurs when the drivers or receivers are not perfectly symmetric. In Figure 2.10 an ideal symmetrical differential signal is shown with red $V_{D+}$ and $V_{D-}$ resulting in consistent signal crossing at the same voltage point. This symmetry provides an equivalent UI width for consecutive UI.

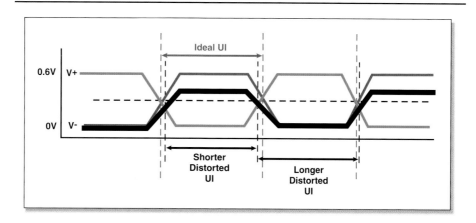

**Figure 2.10** Duty Cycle Distortion

If the differential signals are asymmetric (in the case shown with $V_{D-}$ in gray) the signal crossing voltage difference for consecutive UI will cause one UI to be longer and the subsequent UI to be shorter, alternating the widths for consecutive even and odd UI.

DCD is a common form of deterministic jitter, which can be easily seen in jitter profile distributions as shown in Figure 2.11. UI-UI jitter, since DCD is an even/odd, or bimodal cycle repeated occurrence, is typically pronounced, but may be somewhat masked by the level of random jitter. The "dual peak" profile of the asymmetric even and odd UI widths are more pronounced as N gets larger due to the averaging effect of the more symmetric random jitter.

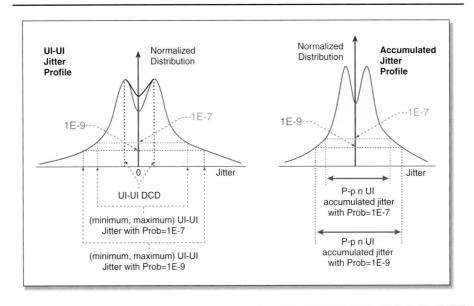

**Figure 2.11** DCD Bimodal Jitter Distribution

### AC and DC Common Mode Voltage

Although Intel QPI signaling is differential, there are two types of common mode voltage requirements: AC and DC common mode voltage. DC common mode voltage is the long-term average DC voltage of the two differential signals. AC common mode voltage is the variation of each UI average voltage compared to the long-term DC common mode voltage as shown in Figure 2.12.

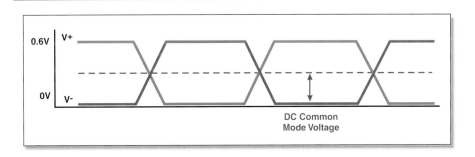

**Figure 2.12** DC Common Mode Voltage

DC common mode voltage is the mean voltage of the $V_{D+}$ and $V_{D-}$ signals over a large sampling of UI as shown in

$$V_{DC\text{-}Common} = mean(0.5(V_{D+} + V_{D-})_i) \quad i=1,2,\ldots,M$$

The specific sampling and duration details are outlined in Chapter 6. It is important to keep the range of DC common mode limited since both the transmitter and receiver are DC coupled and ground referenced. Also, receivers may be sensitive to absolute DC signal offset, so this DC common mode needs to be controlled for receiver input sensitivity.

AC common mode voltage is the mean voltage of each UI compared to the DC common mode voltage. Since each UI may have a different $V_{D+}$ and $V_{D-}$, as well as a different crossing voltage point, the AC common mode voltage may be different for each UI. Figure 2.13 shows AC common mode for a UI contrasted with DC common mode voltage. The range of variation for each UI compared to the DC common mode voltage is specified as the AC common mode voltage and shown as

$$(V_{AC\text{-}Common})_i = (0.5(V_{D+}+V_{D-})_i - V_{DC\text{-}Common}) \quad i =1,2,\ldots,M$$

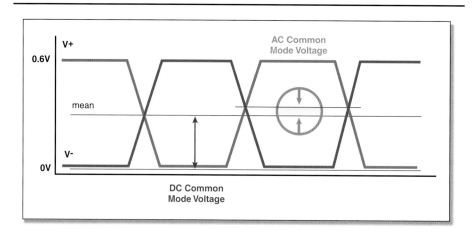

**Figure 2.13** AC Common Mode versus DC Common Mode

## Electrical Specifications

Intel QuickPath Interconnect has two basic categories of electrical specifications: *common specifications* and *platform-dependent specifications*. Common specifications are also referred to as platform-independent specifications, and are applied to all of the specifications that have the same definition and specification values across all components and platform types. Platform-dependent specifications may be defined differently or have different values for different platform types. For example, the Transmitter output differential voltage swing voltage ($V_{Tx-diff-pp-pin}$) may need to be stronger to drive a 2-connector 24" channel topology compared to a 0-connector 14" channel topology. So the 2-connector 24" channel and the 0-connector 14" channel topologies would be two different sets of specifications.

There are common specifications that apply to the reference clock, transmitters and receivers, including data and forwarded clock signals. This allows circuit designs to target single spec values where possible, which simplifies circuit design, and enhances component interoperability and platform flexibility, where a specific circuit is re-used in different components. There are also platform-dependent specifications that ensure the components provide the required performance for individual platform or component needs.

This section first describes the common specification concepts for the reference clock, transmitter and receiver requirements. Then the platform-dependent specification concepts are described for transmitters and receivers (including forwarded clock signals at the transmitter and receiver points). For reference, some of the key common specification parameters list the actual specification values. Since the platform-dependent specifications are not single-valued or unique, these specification values are not listed as they depend on the individual component and platform cases.

As a final note, the common and platform-dependent specification concepts described will be covered in more detail in Chapter 6. The emphasis here is to illustrate the key specification characteristics.

## Common Specifications

Common specifications apply to transmit, receive, and reference clock signals. Some of the parameters apply to both transmitter and receiver, and some apply to only the reference clock. As mentioned earlier, the purpose of the common parameters is to reduce the design, implementation, validation and measurement complexity, and cost.

Some of the parameters are UI-based, and defined for either logical or validation setup purposes (common UI-based parameters). There are specific termination state parameters that have common values for all platforms (common termination parameters). Then there are parameters that are for only the transmitter (common transmitter parameters) and reference clock (reference clock parameters). There are also common parameters for receiver margining; however these will be covered in Chapter 6 in detail, and just mentioned here in this list. So, we have common parameters in these five categories:

- Common UI-based Parameters
- Common termination parameters
- Common transmitter parameters
- Reference clock parameters
- Receiver margining parameters

*Common UI-based Parameters*

The UI-based parameters are mainly defined for logical design compatibility and parameter validation setup. These UI specifications are applied to all operational and debug data and forwarded clock frequencies, so that the terms are consistent, but the size of the UI depends upon the frequency. One parameter listed here is not specifically "UI-based", but fits best with the other parameters ($T_{INBAND\_RESET\_SENSE}$). Otherwise, all of these parameters are defined in terms of UI.

The key common UI-based parameter for Intel QPI channel performance is the bit error rate per lane ($BER_{Lane}$). The BER needs to be met for all platform types and channel topologies, across all manufacturing, temperature, voltage, and process variations. This parameter specifies the bit error rate per lane, so each of the link channels (lanes) must be designed to meet the BER withstanding effects of loss and jitter, reflections, coupling, mode conversion, and other sources of performance degradation.

BER is the ultimate measure of lane data signal integrity between two components. For receiver voltage and timing margining, this is the measure of "goodness" to map out the receiver data eye, to compare to the voltage and timing margin specifications. This bit error rate is the "raw" error rate before any CRC error detection and link layer re-transmission takes place. The value is $1.0 \times 10^{-14}$ events per lane, which means that one bit error (one UI error) is allowed in $1.0 \times 10^{14}$ UI.

Clearly to meet the BER, other common UI-based global parameters need to be defined. First of all, the average UI size, based on the data signaling frequency must be established. The parameter defined for this is $UI_{avg}$, which specifies the average UI size at each data transfer rate, including a minimum and maximum variation from the average. The specification units are picoseconds, and the specification nominal value is 1000/f, where *f* denotes the transfer rate in terms of GigaTransfers/Second. For example, for 4.8 GT/s, f = 4.8.

For signal validation and measurement setup, the test definitions, measurement equipment and scripts need to define the time or duration to perform the specification measurements. To allow for consistency and to reduce setup and measurement complexity, the minimum duration for the voltage and timing specification measurements is specified by the parameter $N_{MIN-UI-Validation}$.

In addition to the UI-based parameters defined for signal quality measurement and validation, some UI-based specifications for data and forwarded clock signals need to be common to all components and platforms for Intel® QPI signaling logical operation. These parameters are all required to be met during specific states within the link initialization, which are included in the descriptions below.

$T_{DATA\_TERM\_SKEW}$: During a link initialization or other state transition in which the receiver (Rx) data lane termination impedances transition to the "on" termination, or $Z_{RX\_LOW\_CM\_DC}$. This is the time between the first receiver data lane and the last data lane reaching this termination state. The different termination state specifications are described in more detail below in the Common Termination Parameters section.

$T_{INBAND\_RESET\_SENSE}$: The inband reset is generated by stopping the forwarded clock between component transmit and receive ports. The receiver inband reset detector is required to detect that the forwarded clock has become inactive (forwarded clock pulses have stopped) within a specified time of the initiation of the forwarded clock inband reset.

$T_{CLK\_DET}$ : Once the forwarded clock begins transmitting the clock signal, this parameter specifies the maximum time within which the receiver clock detector must observe the clock stability.

$T_{CLK\_FREQ\_DET}$ : Once the forwarded clock stability is detected, this parameter specifies the maximum time for the receiver clock frequency detector to identify whether it is the slow or operational clock frequency.

*Common Termination Parameters*

Intel QuickPath Interconnect defines three termination resistance states: (1) high, (2) link detect, and (3) low termination as shown in Figure 2.14. The high termination state ($Z_{High}$) is defined as the inactive, or "off" state. The link detect state ($Z_{Link\_detect}$) is defined for activation during the link initialization state to electrically sense an active "on" load versus an inactive "off" load. The low state ($Z_{Low}$) is defined for the transmitter and receiver lanes during certain initialization, training, and active signaling states as defined in the Intel QuickPath architecture. A number of different states and conditions apply logically and map to these termination definitions, but are not within the scope of this book. For more information about the termination states, please refer to *Weaving High Performance Multiprocessor Fabric*, Maddox et al., Intel Press, 2009.

The high and link detect termination values are common specifications. The low termination value itself is a platform-dependent specification (to allow platform performance optimization for PHY1, PHY2 and PHY3 topologies). The low termination variability (%) however, is a common specification to maintain a common variation across platforms and components that need to interoperate.

The high impedance termination state is defined for transmitters and receivers, for data and forwarded clock signals. For the transmitter, the parameter is $Z_{TX\_HIGH\_CM\_DC}$, and for the receiver it is $Z_{RX\_HIGH\_CM\_DC}$. Since this applies the same to forwarded clock and data signals, it is specified the same for both. This termination state is the effective "off" state, which must be at least 10,000 ohms.

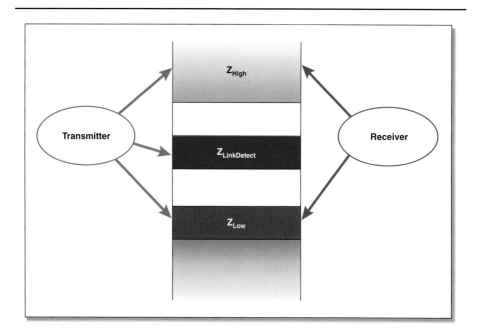

**Figure 2.14** Tx and Rx Termination Ranges

The link detect specifications apply to the transmitter only, since the transmitter provides the link detect circuit to detect the receiver circuit termination state. The link detect circuit has a termination resistance and pull-up voltage specification. Intel QPI employs a DC resistance detection circuit to detect a low "on" termination state (versus "off"). The termination resistance parameter is $Z_{\text{TX\_LINK\_DETECT}}$.

The low termination state is identified by the resultant low voltage due to the stronger low pull-down termination at the receiver versus the link detect termination pull-up at the transmitter, as shown in Figure 2.15. The link detection definition requires a DC-coupled connection between the transmitter and receiver, which is different than PCI Express[†], which uses an AC-coupled connection. The link detect resistance is defined to be within a resistance range safely lower than the "off" and higher than the "on" terminations, between 500 to 2000 ohms to unambiguously sense the difference between the "off" and "on" termination cases.

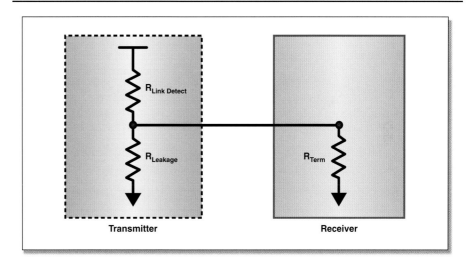

**Figure 2.15** Link Detect Circuit Example

The link detect circuit also specifies the maximum allowed link detect pull-up voltage, which is defined by the parameter $V_{\text{TX\_LINK\_DETECT}}$. This maximum value is specified to prevent agent to agent circuit overstress.

As mentioned earlier, the high and link detect terminations are common specifications across all components and platforms, but the low termination is specific to platforms or channel definitions. The range of termination variation for the low termination, however, is a common specification to provide compatibility within interoperable groups, as well as to set common manufacturing and cost targets for components. The low termination variation has been defined separately for transmitter and receiver to accommodate the different performance challenges of the transmitter and receiver circuits.

$Z_{TX\_LOW\_CM\_DC}$ is the delta or variability specification to the $Z_{TX\_LOW\_CM\_DC}$ (the transmitter termination DC resistance at half the single-ended signal voltage swing, which is defined below in the platform-dependent specification section). This parameter specifies the allowable variation across the full transmitter voltage swing from the $Z_{TX\_LOW\_CM\_DC}$ single-ended resistance. Specifically the definition is:

$$\Delta Z_{TX\text{-}LOW\_CM\_DC} = \pm[\max(\Delta Z_{TX\_LOW\_CM\_DC}) - \min(\Delta Z_{TX\_LOW\_CM\_DC})] / \Delta Z_{TX\_LOW\_CM\_DC}$$

This parameter has the specified value of +/- 6% of $Z_{TX\text{-}LOW\_CM\_DC}$, so it will scale in value depending upon the platform-dependent $Z_{TX\text{-}LOW\_CM\_DC}$ specification value.

$\Delta Z_{RX\_LOW\_CM\_DC}$ is similar to the transmitter termination variability specification ($\Delta Z_{TX\_LOW\_CM\_DC}$), but specifies the receiver variability specification to the $Z_{RX\_LOW\_CM\_DC}$ (the receiver termination DC resistance at half the single-ended signal voltage swing). This parameter specifies the allowable variation across the full receiver voltage swing from the $Z_{RX\_LOW\_CM\_DC}$ single-ended resistance. Specifically the definition is:

$$\Delta Z_{RX\text{-}LOW\_CM\_DC} = \pm[\max(\Delta Z_{RX\_LOW\_CM\_DC}) - \min(\Delta Z_{RX\_LOW\_CM\_DC})] / \Delta Z_{RX\_LOW\_CM\_DC}$$

This parameter, like $Z_{TX\text{-}LOW\_CM\_DC}$, has the specified value of +/- 6 percent of $Z_{RX\text{-}LOW\_CM\_DC}$, so it will scale in value depending upon the platform-dependent $Z_{RX\text{-}LOW\_CM\_DC}$ specification value.

### Common Transmitter Parameters

There are two common transmitter-specific parameters, which are specified at the transmitter pin into a resistive load (assumed to be ~50 ohms). One is the rise and fall time ($T_{slew\text{-}rise\text{-}fall\text{-}pin}$). This is the slope of the rising or falling signal edge within +/- 100 mV of the differential voltage of the data or forwarded clock signals.

The other specification is a measure of the transmitter equalization error ($TX_{EQerror}$). As described in Chapter 1, and illustrated in Figure 1.12, the Intel QPI transmitter equalization provides the capability to apply amplitude conditioning to the current UI (cursor), trailing UI (post-cursor, second post-cursor, and so on) and preceding UI (pre-cursor). Each of these amplitude control circuits are combined, or superimposed on the consecutive UI bit-stream to amplify or dampen the selected UI as shown in Figure 2.16.

The number of equalization taps in a transmitter is not limited or specified, but typically will range between two (cursor, post-cursor) and four (pre-cursor, cursor, first post-cursor, second post-cursor) as shown in this example, in which the pre-cursor is denoted $C_{-1}$, the cursor is $C_0$, and the two post-cursors are $C_1$ and $C_2$.

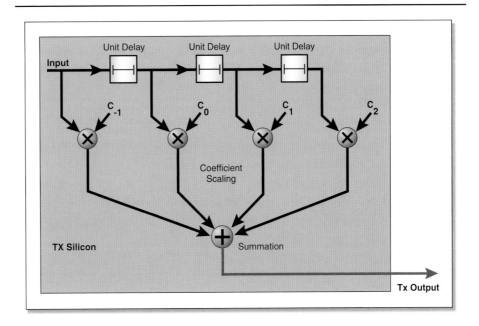

**Figure 2.16** Transmitter Output Equalization

The allowed transmitter equalization error, $TX_{EQerror}$, is the allowed error when measuring the transmitter equalization de-emphasized voltage ($V_{0\_de\_m}$) compared to theoretical (calculated) de-emphasized voltage ($V_{0\_de}$). This is not an AC specification. It is a DC differential specification, with the $V_0$ representing the fully emphasized differential output voltage. The error allowed is +/- 10 percent of $V_0$.

*Reference Clock Parameters*

The reference clock is also called the system reference clock or system clock. The clock frequency is common across all components and platforms, with a value of 133.3333 MHz for all current products. The other reference clock parameter definitions and values are also common across all components and platforms.

All of the reference clocks for the Intel QPI components that are interconnected by links originate from a single clock source. All of these components are defined to be within a single clock domain. The reference clock frequency among all components must be the same, but the phase or edge alignment may be different comprising a fixed skew between component reference clock inputs.

The reference clock is a differential signal, but some of the specifications are validated as differential and some as single-ended signals. The specific validation definitions are covered in Chapter 6.

The single-ended specifications include positive and negative overvoltage limits, $V_{Refclk-Max}$ and $V_{Refclk-Min}$ respectively, which are the absolute voltage swing values with respect to ground as shown in Figure 2.17. Also specified as single-ended specifications are the $V_{Cross}$ and $V_{Cross-delta}$, which are a measure of the absolute voltage average D+ and D- cross point and the range of variation of the crossing points.

The $V_{Refclk-Max}$ and $V_{Refclk-Min}$ parameters are the single-ended overshoot and undershoot (also referred to as negative overshoot). These voltages are not to be exceeded during normal device operation, generally for stress/reliability considerations. The $V_{Refclk-max}$ is not to exceed 1150 mV and the $V_{Refclk-min}$ is not to be more negative than -300 mV.

The $V_{cross}$ parameter represents the absolute DC voltage crossing point limits between the Refclk+ and Refclk- signal waveforms. To ensure that the DC voltage range of the signal crossing is met for the receiver sensitivity design, this crossing must be within a DC voltage range of 250 mV (minimum) and 550mV (maximum).

To accommodate noise variation around the $V_{Cross}$ voltage, $V_{Cross\_delta}$ specifies how much differential voltage cross point variation is allowed during operation. The peak-to-peak variation in crossing points is 140 mV (maximum).

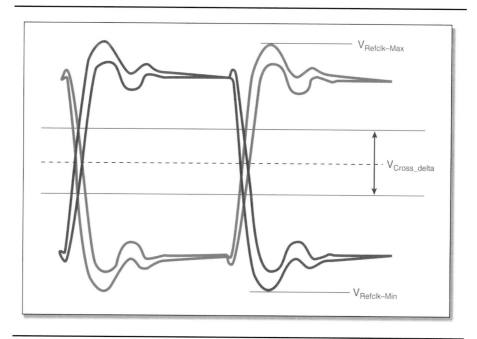

**Figure 2.17** Reference Clock Single-ended Specifications

The reference clock differential specifications include the clock frequency ($f_{Refclk}$), signal rise and fall edge rate ($ER_{Refclk-diffRise}$, $ER_{Refclk-diffFall}$), minimum high and low voltage ($V_{Refclk-diff-ih}$, $V_{Refclk-diff-il}$), duty cycle ($T_{Refclk-Dutycycle}$) and jitter ($T_{Refclk-jitter-rms-onepll}$). These specifications are illustrated in Figure 2.18.

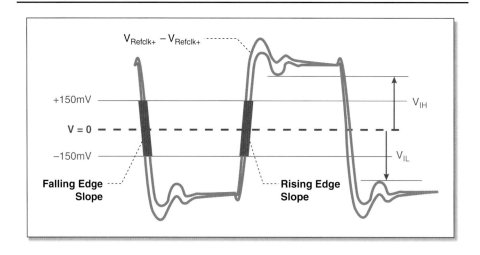

**Figure 2.18** Reference Clock Differential Specifications

The reference clock frequency, $f_{Refclk}$, has been selected as a common frequency, based on the power versus jitter constraints. For general guidance, a higher clock frequency will provide better (lower) jitter, but at the expense of power. A lower clock frequency will consume less power at the expense of higher jitter.

The reference clock and forwarded clock phase timing relationship is critical to lane-to-lane skew management. The key relationship that needs to be maintained is not the specific phase itself, but the variation, or drift, of phase over time.

The two key parameters defined for this are the reference clock phase variation at each component reference clock input ($T_{Refclk-diff-jit}$) and the reference clock to forwarded clock phase variation ($T_{Refclk-Tx-Variability}$). The combination of these two parameters comprises the phase drift between any two components with connected Intel QPI ports.

$T_{Refclk-diff-jit}$ specifies the maximum phase drift between any and all of the Intel QPI agents to be no more than 500 pS (which actually means +/- 500 pS between the reference clock inputs of any components). This phase variation is illustrated in Figure 2.19 for two agents, shown as "A".

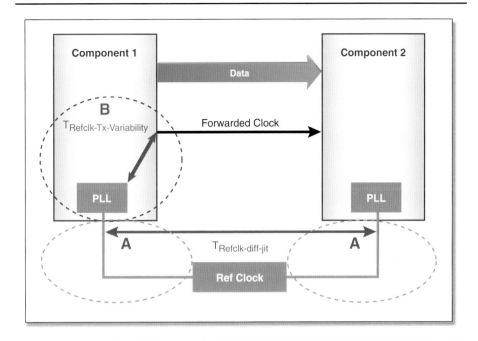

**Figure 2.19** Reference and Forwarded Clock Drift

$T_{Refclk-Tx-Variability}$ specifies the maximum drift between the component reference clock input and forwarded clock output for each component. In Figure 2.19, this is shown as "B". This specification complements the $T_{Refclk-diff-jit}$ specification to limit the total maximum drift between two component links to 1ns (500 ps + 500 ps), so that the total drift over time is bounded. These two parameters are important to limit the overall lane-to-lane deskew range.

## Platform-dependent Specifications

The platform-dependent specifications apply to the transmitter and receiver clock and data signals only. The system reference clock specifications are all common across platforms.

*Transmitter Specifications*

The transmitter specifications may differ between different platform types. Depending upon the data transfer rate, channel, and connector definitions, the transmitter drive and noise specifications need to meet the channel and receiver performance requirements. For each platform type, these transmitter specifications are defined to meet the individual platform characteristics.

The purpose of the transmitter is to effectively transmit valid data signals, with sufficient amplitude, clean signal edges, and controlled impedance to be delivered to the receiver. Because of transmitter design constraints due to power, frequency, process, and physical design requirements, the design capability and limits are different for different channel and platform specific requirements.

The transmitter specifications may be different for the different platform types, but all of the transmitter specifications are validated into a 50-ohm test load as shown in Figure 2.20. Specifically, each data lane signal, D+ and D- are terminated into the 50-ohm load to ground.

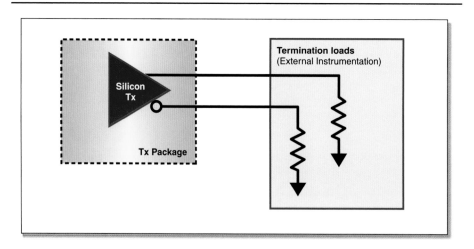

**Figure 2.20** Transmitter Specification Termination

The platform-dependent transmitter parameters defined to provide effective signaling performance are of the following types: Impedance, voltage swing, data and clock jitter, AC/DC common mode voltage, duty cycle, and clock-to-data skew as depicted in Figure 2.21. All of these parameters are required to be met for system signaling performance. All of these parameters apply to the data and forwarded clock transmitters.

The transmitter impedance ($Z_{TX-LOW-CM-DC}$) for the operational (and some link training) states is also called the low termination state. As mentioned in the Common Termination Parameters section, the low termination specification is platform-dependent, unlike the high and link detect states that are common specifications.

The transmitter output voltage swing is specified as a differential peak-to-peak voltage amplitude ($V_{Tx-diff-pp-pin}$). This is the fully emphasized voltage swing without equalization employed. This is platform-dependent due to the difference in signal strength needed for more complex and longer topologies versus simpler and shorter topologies.

The transmitter duty cycle specification ($TX_{duty-pin}$) is the UI-UI variation in UI width. Any two consecutive clock signal UI are generated from the opposite differential signal pair edges. For example the D+ and D- signal for a logical "1" are generated by the D+ rising edge and the D- negative edge. The next UI, which is a logical "0", is generated by the D+ falling edge and D- rising edge. The D- rising edge will typically be different than the D+ rising edge due to process, layout, voltage, and temperature differences between the circuits, as will be the D- and D+ falling edges. Because of these signal edge differences, the odd and even UI have different statistical width profiles and the duty cycle profile is a bimodal distribution, as shown in Figure 2.11. The duty cycle tolerance allowed is different depending upon the challenges of the topology complexity, so needs to be a platform-dependent specification.

The DC and AC common mode specifications ($V_{Tx-cm-dc-pin}$, $V_{Tx-cm-ac-pin}$) are influenced by the complex and lossy interconnect path and elements. In a simple and short topology, with no connectors, the variation in the DC common mode voltage will be minimal compared to a longer lossy interconnect. For the AC common mode voltage, the variation from the DC common mode voltage will also be more aggravated by a longer lossy channel than a short channel. Thus these parameters need to be optimized and defined for the range needed to accommodate the different channel categories.

The transmitter jitter profiles are bimodal distributions, as shown in Figure 2.11. Jitter specifications fall into two categories. One is the UI-UI jitter, which is the jitter between any two consecutive UI ($T_{XjitUI-UI-1E-7pin}$, $T_{XjitUI-UI-1E-9pin}$). The other jitter is the N-UI jitter ($T_{Xclk-acc-jit-N\_UI-1E-7}$, $T_{Xclk-acc-jit-N\_UI-1E-9}$), which is specified for a consecutive series of N-UI, where N is 12.

Due to the extremely large number of UI that would need to be sampled to directly measure the voltage distributions for BER of one error in $10^{14}$ UI, the two alternate (1E-7, 1E-9) specifications are defined. One is measured at a distribution for one error in $10^7$ UI and the other is for one error in $10^9$ UI. The voltage profiles are measured to correspond to these error rates, which are then used to tail-fit to predict the error rate at $10^{14}$. For the 1E-7 specification, $10^8$ UI are sampled and for the 1E-9, $10^{10}$ UI are sampled. The validation approach is covered in Chapter 6.

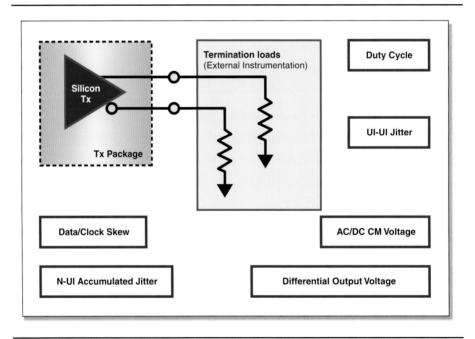

**Figure 2.21** Transmitter Specifications

The discussion of the final transmitter specification covered here is combined with that of the same type of receiver specification, since both are a measure of skew, or phase difference, between the data and forwarded clock signal. One is measured at the transmitter output pin ($T_{\text{Tx-data-clk-skew-pin}}$), and the other is measured at the receiver input pin ($T_{\text{Rx-data-clk-skew-pin}}$) as shown in Figure 2.22.

The data to forwarded clock skew at the transmitter, $T_{\text{Tx-data-clk-skew-pin}}$, is a measure of the transmitter silicon and package introduced skew. It limits minimum and maximum edge placement difference across all data lanes at the transmitter output pins. Similarly, at the receiver input pin, all of the data lanes are limited to a minimum and maximum skew with respect to the received forwarded clock.

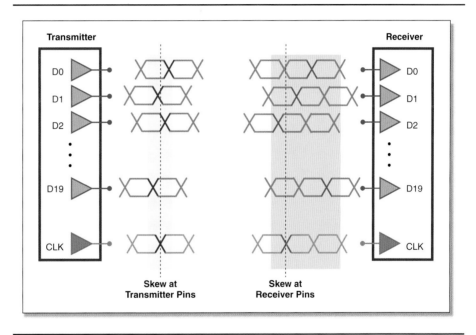

**Figure 2.22** Intel® QPI Tx and Rx Data to Forwarded Clock Skew

The minimum to maximum skew range at the receiver pins ($T_{\text{Rx-data-clk-skew-pin}}$) is greater than at the transmitter, allowing some PCB signal trace routing flexibility. This is a platform-dependent specification since the more extreme topologies such as the PHY1 are typically longer length and have more connectors, so the routing challenges are greater and expected amount of performance variation is also greater than for the simpler topologies. Consequently, the minimum and maximum skew range is larger for the PHY1 than for the PHY3 topology.

*Receiver Specifications*

The receiver specifications may also differ between different platform types, depending upon the data transfer rate, channel and connector definitions. Depending upon the data transfer rate, channel and connector definitions, the receiver sensitivity needs to meet the transmitter and channel performance requirements. For each platform, these receiver specifications are defined to meet the individual platform characteristics.

The purpose of the receiver is to effectively detect and receive valid data signals, with sufficient amplitude and controlled impedance for a given channel. Because of receiver design constraints due to power, frequency, process and physical design requirements, the design capability and limits are different for different channel and platform requirements.

The platform-dependent receiver parameters defined to provide effective signaling performance are of the following types: Impedance, signal voltage and timing margin, data and clock jitter, AC/DC common mode voltage, and clock-to-data skew. All of these parameters are required to be met for system signaling performance. All of these parameters apply to the data and forwarded clock receiver lanes.

Most of these receiver parameters are either margined, by use of a bit error rate tester (BERT), as shown in Figure 2.23, or forced inputs. Two of the receiver parameters are measured directly: $Z_{RX\_LOW\_CM\_DC}$, the "on" state impedance, and the receiver data to clock skew $T_{Tx\text{-}data\text{-}clk\text{-}skew\text{-}pin}$ (see Figure 2.22). The receiver "on" impedance is a DC measurement at the receiver pin, and the data to clock skew measurement is performed in-system at the receiver input point (please refer to Chapter 6).

The basic setup to validate the receiver parameters requires the BERT to send a data pattern on the data lanes and a forwarded clock, so that the data and clock inputs may be both individually varied, and varied with respect to each other to map out the data and clock performance margins.

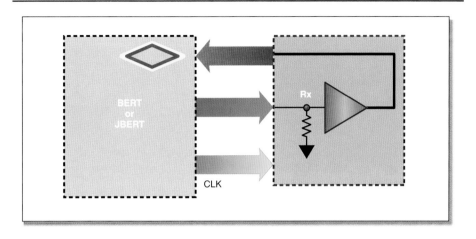

**Figure 2.23** Receiver Basic Margining Setup with Bit Error Rate Tester

The margined receiver parameters include the data voltage and timing margins ($V_{Rx\text{-}Vmargin}$, $T_{Rx\text{-}Tmargin}$, $T_{Rx\text{-}margin}$, $V_{Rx\text{-}margin}$) and the clock voltage margin ($V_{Rx\text{-}CLK}$) as generically shown in Figure 2.24. The validation of these parameters is covered in detail in Chapter 6.

The forced receiver parameters are provided by the BERT at the receiver input. For the receiver data inputs, the AC and DC common mode voltages ($V_{Rx\text{-}cm\text{-}dc\text{-}pin}$, $V_{Rx\text{-}cm\text{-}ac\text{-}pin}$) are applied during the receiver voltage and timing margining tests as shown in Figure 2.24. For the forwarded clock margin testing, the clock duty cycle distortion ($T_{Rx\text{-}DCD\text{-}CLK}$) is applied during the forwarded clock voltage margining tests.

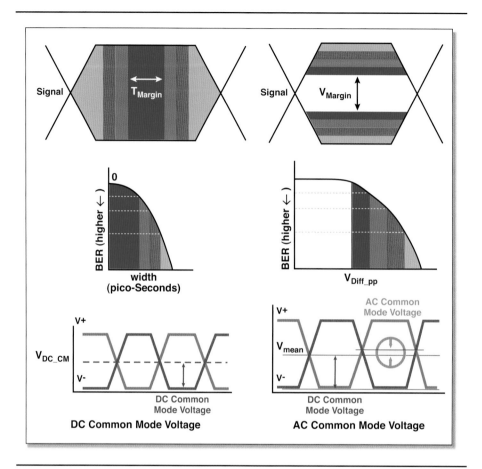

**Figure 2.24** Receiver Margining Parameters

# Chapter 3

# Controlling the Impact of Signal Integrity Phenomena

The objective of any electrical system design, from a signal integrity perspective, is to ensure that the signals transmitted by driving components are received without distortion significant enough to corrupt the data represented by those signals. For both parallel and serial-differential bus designs, the primary factors to consider and control are

- Signal delay
- Crosstalk
- Reflective effects
- Signal attenuation or loss
- Jitter

Each of these is discussed in this chapter. Note that most of the concepts discussed here apply both to Intel® QuickPath Interconnect (Intel® QPI) and many other serial-differential and even single-ended interface designs. While these areas cannot be treated in any other than a cursory way here, recommended sources for additional information are provided in the References section.

After the general signal integrity factors are reviewed, the contributions to each by the major components of typical Intel QPI platforms are discussed. Methods to analyze and mitigate these effects are also covered.

## Signal Delay

Systems based on transmission lines have a certain physical delay associated with the time taken for signals to move from transmitter to receiver. Even in a lossless system, signals do not move instantaneously from one end of a system to the other. The time taken for the signals to traverse the system is called signal delay.

This delay is determined by the physical and electrical properties of the medium through which the signals move (that is, the dielectric of the material surrounding the signal-carrying wires and the physical dimensions of the wires themselves). For serial-differential systems, pure signal delay is not a significant issue except where a specific timing relationship must be maintained between data pairs, or between data and clock signals (for a notable exception, see the electrical chapter of the USB 2.0 specification). In the case of Intel QPI, both the Intel QPI specification and the individual platform design guidelines (PDGs) provide guidance on any critical timing relationships to maintain. In general, the absolute travel time taken by Intel QPI signals is not constrained, though the relative time between some signals may be. Note that a subtle difference exists between pure signal delay and the industry terms "propagation delay" and "flight time," which refer to the difference in signals observed between a driver and receiver, where reflections, degradation due to loss, and other effects may be included.

## Crosstalk

Crosstalk is simply the impact of one signal on another. In the system context, this is due to electromagnetic coupling between signal-carrying media in close proximity. Crosstalk can occur in any medium, whether connector or cable routes, PCB or package traces or even vias.

Crosstalk in a digital system is an AC phenomenon, appearing only when signals change state. The mechanisms for crosstalk are inductive coupling and capacitive coupling. In inductive coupling, one can consider the signal medium as a wire. As the signal changes state and therefore the amount of current through the wire changes, it generates a magnetic field. Any other wire-like structures in the generated magnetic field will "see" some amount of energy from the signal wire, as shown in Figure 3.1. The strength of the coupled magnetic field depends on the amount of energy in the wire and the distance between the victim wire and the signal wire.

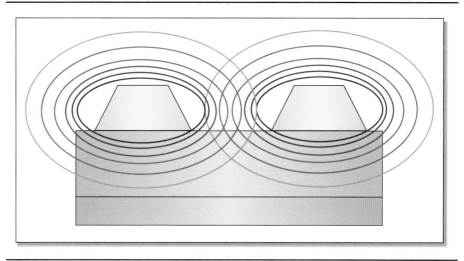

**Figure 3.1**    Magnetic Field Coupling in a Differential Pair

Capacitive coupling is conceptually similar, except that the coupling mechanism is an electric field generated by the time-varying voltage in the signal wire, as illustrated in Figure 3.2. Again, any wire-like structure within the field will experience coupling effects whose strength is determined by the amount of energy in the original wire, the properties of the material separating the wires, and the distance between the wires.

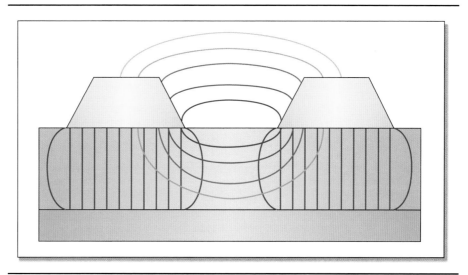

**Figure 3.2**    Electrical Field Coupling in a Differential Pair

Crosstalk is a key concern in signal integrity, and the effects of crosstalk are usually captured by modeling the signal traces and their coupling effects directly, through a field solver, as explained later in this section and in Chapter 4. Crosstalk can increase or reduce the amount of cumulative signal seen at any particular time point (due to constructive or destructive interference, respectively). This can reduce voltage margin or timing margin or both.

## NEXT and FEXT

For differential systems, near-end crosstalk (NEXT) and far-end crosstalk (FEXT) are important concepts, illustrated in Figure 3.3. These are often used to characterize multi-conductor systems such as cables and connectors. As implied by the name, NEXT is simply the crosstalk between a transmitting signal and a neighbor, when both are measured at the transmitting (near) "end" of a differential system. FEXT is the crosstalk between a transmitting signal and a neighbor when the amount of energy on the neighbor is measured at the "end" of the system opposite the transmitter. In this way, both electromagnetic coupling and loss are included in the FEXT measurement. Some S-parameters data sets are called NEXT and FEXT, depending on the port orientation of the transmitter and interconnect "ends" (for example, a two-line, four-port system's NEXT would be S13, if one line had ports 1 and 2 as its near and far endpoints respectively, with the other line having lines 3 and 4 as its endpoints, arranged similarly).

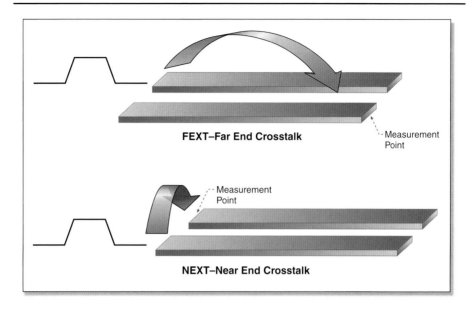

**Figure 3.3**   NEXT and FEXT

The impact of crosstalk can be included in an overall system budget (eye diagram, for example) used for simulation or validation. In the case of Intel QPI, the peak distortion analysis (PDA) technique accounts for overall topology crosstalk through Signal Integrity Simulation Tools for Advanced Interfaces (SISTAI), a web-based suite of tools provided for Intel customers, described in more detail in Chapter 4. The simulation flow used to provide inputs to SISTAI assumes simulation of a three-pair, six-signal system, which will normally include crosstalk in the interconnects, including package, board, connectors, vias, and any other medium in which crosstalk has been modeled.

## Reflective Effects

One of the primary problems affecting high-speed system designs is poor signal quality from reflections. Just as acoustical energy can "bounce" around a large room or wave fronts on the surface of a body of water can interact, electrical energy can reflect off of discontinuous areas in a signal path.

The problem with such interactions is that the energy from incoming and outgoing waves can constructively or destructively sum, causing apparent signal increases or attenuation, respectively. Should these effects occur at the receiver, the signal and therefore the data stream at the receiver can become corrupted or the receiver could be damaged.

In a concert hall, the placement of objects in the physical space and their sound absorption properties determine how the acoustical energy is perceived by the listener. If the space between the listener and the sound source is un-obstructed and has uniform properties, and if the sound energy dies away before hitting the walls, the listener will perceive what the sound source generates without distortion, minus energy losses. Similarly, the placement and electrical properties of the system media determine the distortion of the signal at the receiver. The electrical impedance of the traces, vias, connectors, cables, and so on between the driver and receiver, plus the driver and receiver impedances themselves, have an enormous impact on the quality of the signal at the receiver.

Impedance, while a critical concept, is too large a topic to be addressed in depth here. Formally, impedance is the numerical relationship between time-varying electrical and magnetic fields. For the purposes of signal integrity, impedance is (as the name suggests) a quantitative measure of how easily time-varying signals pass into or through an electromagnetic medium.

In a system design where many different components may be connected (such as vias, traces, transmitters, receivers, and connectors), reflections occur when impedances of each of the connected components are mismatched. For example, a high impedance termination on a low impedance transmission line will cause significant amounts of energy to "bounce" off the termination and return to the driving signal source, potentially causing significant distortions for current and subsequent data at the receiver.

When a system topology contains components or PCB segments with different impedances (such as backplanes and cards), reflections can result as the driven signal encounters the impedance mismatches and "bounces" between them. These reflections can destructively or constructively interfere with subsequent driven bits, respectively reducing or increasing the effective voltages per bit seen at the receiver. Impedances can vary for many reasons. These include device variations, such as pad capacitance, package vertical path variations, and termination variance. These can also result from interconnect variations in sockets, PCB vias, and connectors. Finally, the PCB itself can contribute variations and mismatches, from layer transitions, and PCB-to-package and PCB layer-to-layer variations over high volume manufacturing (HVM).

Methods to determine the impedance of various components for the purposes of signal integrity modeling are described later in the chapter. For most purposes, the ideal approach is to match impedances from component to component in a system signal path, or at least to tune the component impedances to reduce signal distortions at the receiver.

## Impedance Matching

For the most part, trace impedance is the most malleable impedance of any component in a PCB system. Device and connector impedances are controlled by their respective manufacturers. Via impedances will be constrained by PCB stackup and manufacturing choices, such as barrel and anti-pad size. Trace impedances, however, can be controlled through geometry decisions even if stackup and material choices have already been taken.

Single-ended characteristic impedance (hereafter, simply impedance) in a PCB trace is determined by its physical properties, including the dimensions of the trace and its distance from its reference. The material properties of the dielectric material and the trace itself are also critical. As a simple approximation, the impedance of a trace in a lossless sense can be computed from the capacitance of the trace with respect to its reference, and the inductance of the trace-reference loop, in the following equation:

$$Zo = \sqrt{\frac{Lo}{Co}}$$

where Zo is the impedance in ohms per unit length, Lo is the inductance in henries per unit length and Co is the capacitance in farads per unit length. Note how this neatly conveys how impedance is a relationship between electrical and magnetic fields—inductance represents the magnetic field contribution while capacitance represents the electric field contribution. More precise impedance information for individual components, including loss effects, can be determined from measurement or simulation.

In differential PCB systems, two impedance relationships should be managed: differential and common-mode. As with single-ended impedance, differential and common-mode impedances are determined by the physical and material properties of the traces and trace medium. However, common-mode impedance need not be managed directly. By controlling both the differential impedance of the trace pair and the single-ended impedances of each line in the pair, the common-mode impedances will be constrained. This will become obvious from the equations used to determine differential and common-mode impedances.

The differential impedance characterizes the relationship within a signal pair where the signal lines are switching in opposition (or odd mode, where voltages are complementary). The potential difference between the signals in the pair imply capacitive coupling separate from the capacitance of each signal to any nearby reference (PCB systems usually involve some reference plane as close or closer to the signals as the signals are to each other) as shown in Figure 3.4.

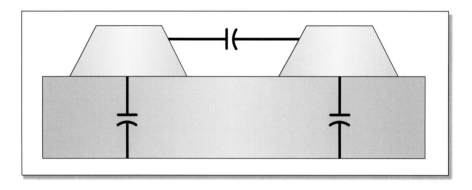

**Figure 3.4**   Simplified Representation of Capacitive Coupling

A common mathematical treatment of differential impedance for a pair of identical traces is

$$Zdiff = 2 * Zodd = 2 * (Z11 - Z12)$$

where all the impedances are in ohms, Z11 is the single-ended impedance of either of the traces, and Z12 is the impedance of signal 1 to signal 2, neglecting effects of any nearby reference plane.

Common-mode impedance characterizes the relationship of the pair's signals when they both switch in an identical fashion (voltages are identical). The lines therefore have the same potential relative to any reference, and any capacitive coupling effects between them therefore vanish.

A typical mathematical treatment of common-mode impedance for a pair of identical traces is

$$Zcommon = \frac{Zeven}{2} = \frac{(Z11 + Z12)}{2}$$

where all the impedances are in ohms, Z11 is the single-ended impedance of either of the traces, and Z12 is the ratio of the voltage on signal 1 to the current on signal 2, with respect to the nearby reference plane.[1]

Again, the primary objective behind determining and controlling differential and common-mode impedances is to ensure that discontinuities are minimized between areas of interconnect. Reflections and attendant negative effects will therefore be reduced or eliminated. Note that impedances may not always be matched across the entire interface to achieve optimum signal integrity performance. While the Intel QPI system target impedance is 85 ohms, PCI Express[†] for server platforms tends to combine 85-ohm interconnects with 100-ohm devices for optimum signal integrity.[2] Investigation and optimization of impedance based on performance is recommended.

## Loss

Loss, as the name suggests, is the transformation of electrical energy into some form not useful for signal transmission. This may be in the form of radiation, where the transmitted energy leaves the signal medium entirely, which may result in crosstalk effects, or electromagnetic interference (EMI) with other devices. It may also be in the form of heating, due to resistive effects or charge storage in the transmission medium.

---

1   One key reason these equations are at best simplifications is that PCB traces, as well as other devices, have frequency-dependent impedances, usually expressed in real and imaginary or other equivalent terms. As a result, matching may be possible only over a limited frequency range.

2   This is primarily due to the physical design parameters needed to achieve 85-ohm differential target impedances in typical systems. For typical computer systems, traces are usually wider in 85-ohm designs than in 100-ohm designs, and dielectrics may also be thinner.

The practical effect of loss is the attenuation of the signal at the receiver relative to what was transmitted.

Losses may be actual or apparent. For example, energy radiated from the transmitting medium is truly lost to the receiver and the system as a whole. However, the receiver may see an attenuated signal due to reflections causing destructive interference. In this case, the energy is still present in the system, as can be shown if the reflections were reduced (for example, by changing the receiver's distance to the transmitter or improving the impedance matching in the interconnect).

Note that technical literature refers to *dispersive losses.* These are apparent losses resulting from different frequencies encountering different amounts of attenuation, as most materials do not exhibit flat attenuations across all frequencies. Compensating for such losses is a primary motivation for equalization.

For PCBs, the two major mechanisms for loss are the resistive losses of the traces (both at DC and as a function of frequency) and the frequency-dependent charge absorption of the dielectric. The literature refers to these as trace losses, skin-effect losses, and dielectric losses, respectively.

In an Intel QPI system, the primary loss mechanism is the PCB trace routing. Here, loss is strongly correlated with the length of the trace routes. Reducing trace lengths can reduce real losses. However, apparent losses from inter-symbol interference (ISI) due to impedance mismatches may be made worse if trace lengths are reduced enough to place the receiver at a resonance point for destructive interference. Again, optimization of trace design (losses and impedances) is a primary goal of signal integrity simulation. Additional guidance on trace impacts on signal integrity are given later in the chapter and in Chapter 4.

## Jitter

Jitter is the deviation, usually in time, between when a signal is expected and when it arrives. Jitter is also a highly complex topic that cannot be treated fully in a short chapter.

For serial-differential systems, jitter is usually split into deterministic and random components. Deterministic jitter results from periodic or predictable sources (for example, clock sources inside the transmitter and/or receiver).

Random jitter is essentially unpredictable for individual occurrences, resulting from cosmic rays, thermal effects, or other nonperiodic events. Over multiple occurrences, random jitter may be approximated statistically.

While active devices are strong sources of jitter, system interconnects can contribute to deterministic jitter. First, jitter can be made worse by reflective effects and crosstalk. Noise that "moves" where a signal edge is relative to an ideal crossing point, for example, will result in jitter at the receiver. Similarly, even without impedance discontinuities and noise coupling, interconnect losses can degrade signal edges sufficiently to change the timing of how the signals are latched by the receiver (this is called *jitter amplification*).

Even only one or two misplaced edges can result in jitter impact sufficient to reduce eye diagram widths and therefore system margins as shown in Figure 3.5 and Figure 3.6 (details on eye diagrams are provided later in this chapter).

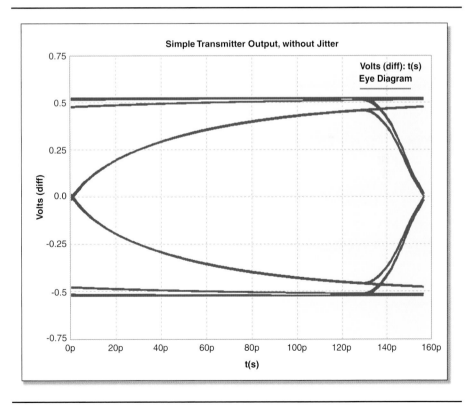

**Figure 3.5**  Eye Diagram for Simple Transmitter with Minimal Jitter

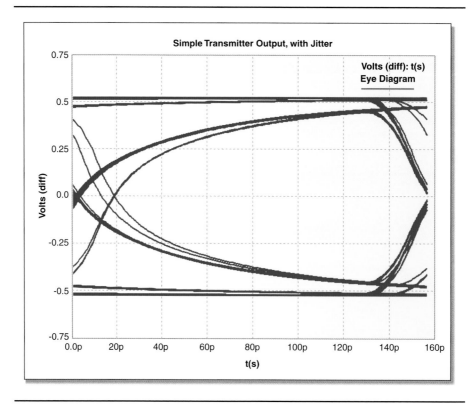

**Figure 3.6**   Eye Diagram for Simple Transmitter with Added Jitter

Both deterministic and random jitter types can be budgeted into system analysis. However, only deterministic jitter can be directly included in analog simulations (for example, by changing the data pattern supplied to the transmitting device). Trace loss, crosstalk and ISI are of course effects of primary interest in signal integrity simulations. Random jitter effects are analyzed through statistical methods, based on known or assumed distributions of the driver, receiver, and other components.

For Intel QPI systems in signal integrity simulations, most deterministic and random jitter effects have been accounted for in the eye templates provided for analysis. The pulse-based simulations recommended for PDA will include the jitter amplification produced by the system interconnect. While jitter is a major determinant of the performance of an Intel QPI system, the device-driven portions of jitter are outside of the control of PCB system designers, as shown in the contribution approximations in Figure 3.7. PCB system designers should instead focus on minimizing the negative impact of crosstalk and ISI from reflections, to minimize resulting jitter.

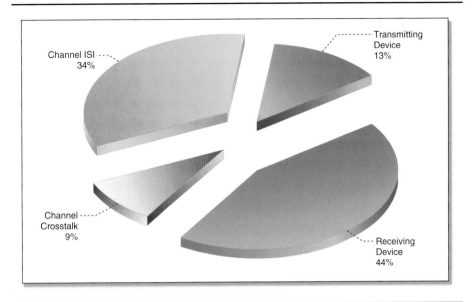

**Figure 3.7**   Contributors to System Jitter in a Theoretical Intel® QuickPath Interconnect 6.4-GT/s System Design

## Differential Routing versus Differential Receivers

One of the most important observations about serial-differential interfaces for most computer systems is that their differential nature comes primarily from how the signal is received, not how the signal is routed.

For single-ended signals, the receiver can be considered a comparator, with the incoming signal being compared with a separate reference. This reference is a voltage level provided by a voltage divider or similar circuitry. The output of the comparator is a logic level presented to the logic core. The reference voltage may be subject to local supply noise effects that distort the output. Similarly, noise on the incoming signal due to crosstalk or similar effects will have a direct impact on the logic level presented to the logic core. Figure 3.8

shows a system featuring a receiver that is referenced to local power supplies. Should noise cause the supply voltage to vary significantly versus the incoming signal, the signal itself could be latched into the logic core incorrectly.

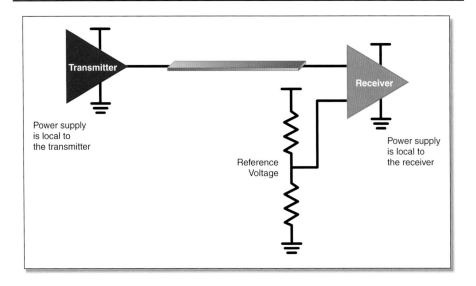

**Figure 3.8**   Single-ended Signaling

A serial-differential system provides some advantages over the single-ended approach. In serial-differential designs, a pair of signals is routed from driver to receiver, with one signal carrying a voltage level complementary (equal and opposite) to the other[3]. The receiver processes the incoming signal by comparing the positive signal in the pair to the negative signal. In other words, the negative signal acts as the reference for the positive signal, with the receiver seeing the difference between the signal levels on the lines in the pair (hence *differential*).[4]

---

3   In most cases. For USB, "out of band" signals may be transmitted that are common mode and convey special information about the state of the system.

4   Note that receivers usually have a DC voltage range over which they correctly operate differentially. For Intel QPI, a ground-referenced DC voltage range is defined in the interface specification.

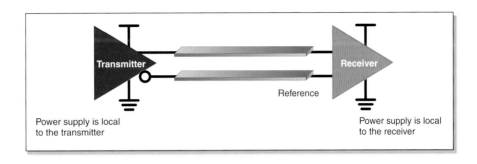

**Figure 3.9**   Differential Signaling

What makes this approach advantageous is that the receiver can exclude or reject noise that affects both incoming signals (called "common mode rejection"). Power supply noise that would distort the reference voltage in a single-ended system would not have any impact on a differential one, as shown in Figure 3.10.

This constrains PCB designs somewhat, in that the geometry and routing of the two signals should be as similar as possible. This ensures that noise effects on the signals are close to identical and may therefore be rejected by the receiving comparator. Similarly, signal losses should be maintained as identically as possible between the two lines, to ensure the difference between them meets the comparator requirements.[5]

What is most important about most server and personal computer serial-differential designs is that the differential nature of the receiver, not the coupling relationship of the traces, makes the system effective. As seen above, the electromagnetic coupling between the traces in a differential pair on a typical PCB stackup is comparatively weak. This means that both signals use a nearby plane as a reference; the positive signal does not primarily use the negative signal as its reference, as would be the case in twisted pair cables, for example. Therefore, the serial-differential designs in typical PCBs used for computer systems do not gain noise immunity from the trace layout. As a consequence, the return paths for the differential pair through nearby planes cannot be ignored.

---

5   Trace length mismatches and reflective effects between the lines should also be kept similar, to reduce jitter effects, as mentioned earlier.

As a practical matter, the routing of differential pairs should be kept as similar as possible. This ensures that the noise effects on both pairs are close to identical and can therefore be rejected by the receiver.

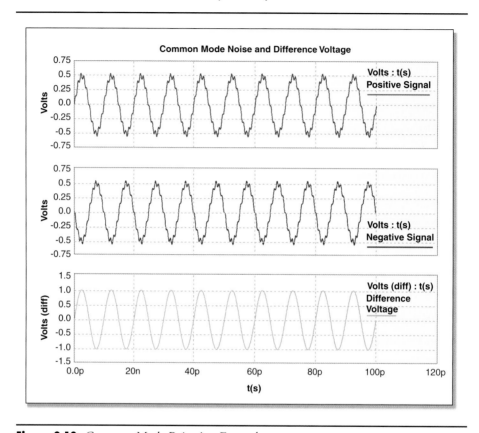

**Figure 3.10** Common Mode Rejection Example

## Drivers and Equalization

As noted in the previous section, the primary effects to be controlled in an Intel QPI topology are ISI, loss, jitter, and crosstalk. Crosstalk is a direct function of the distance between interconnect paths, as related to transmitted signal strength (the interconnect paths can be part of the connectors, cables, PCB traces, PCB vias, or package features). Crosstalk effects are therefore somewhat difficult to overcome using transmitter or receiver design features. ISI, loss, and jitter effects, however, may be mitigated using equalization, as explained below.

Equalization is simply the process of adjusting the signal at the driver or receiver to compensate ("equalize") for the effects of the transmission medium. Energy losses in the path over which the signal travels may result in a garbled signal at the receiving device. The effects of such signal losses are best illustrated in the frequency domain, as shown in Figure 3.11.

The energy from a given transmitted signal has a particular bandwidth or frequency spectrum. Common rules of thumb for calculating the frequency bandwidth of a driven edge include:

$$F_{knee}(zH) = \frac{0.35}{tr(s)}$$

where the knee frequency, in hertz, is the point at which the energy within the driven edge begins to roll off (often called the 3-dB point) and *tr* is the rise time, in seconds, of the driven edge from 20 percent to 80 percent of its full swing. The energy spectrum of a pulse response signal can be obtained by simply taking its Fourier transform, as shown in Figure 3.11 and Figure 3.12 for two different transmitter speeds.

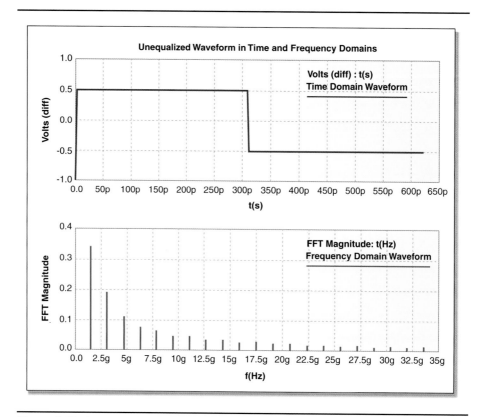

**Figure 3.11** Time- and Frequency-domain Waveforms for Unequalized 3.2 GT/s Transmitter

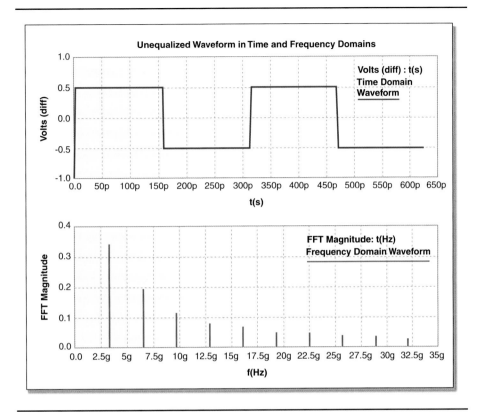

**Figure 3.12**  Time- and Frequency-domain Waveforms for Unequalized 6.4 GT/s
Transmitter

The losses of a PCB trace also have a particular characteristic, where some
frequencies are passed with relatively little loss (usually the lower ones) while
others are highly attenuated. Significant attenuation may reduce the signal
strength below what the receiver can perceive. Equalization, as shown in
Figure 3.13, changes the energy distribution in the transmitted signal, so that
the output signal shows approximately the same loss at lower frequencies as it
does in the higher ones, within the bandwidth of interest.

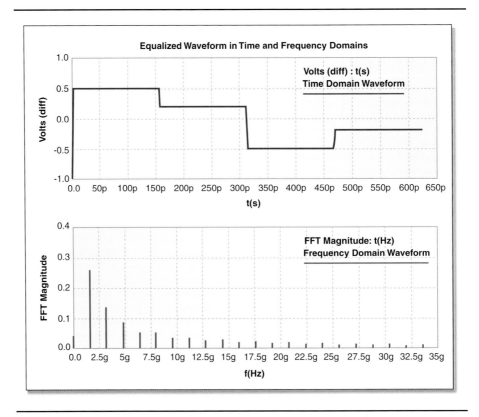

**Figure 3.13** Time- and Frequency-domain Waveforms for Equalized 3.2 GT/s Transmitter

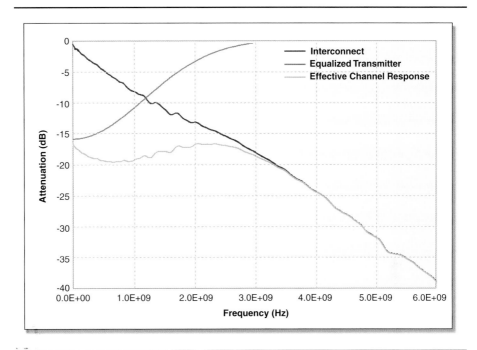

**Figure 3.14** Frequency-domain Response of System with Equalization

Note that this equalization at the transmitter may take the form of boosting or increasing the energy driven at higher frequencies or reducing the energy driven at lower ones, as shown in Figure 3.14. The outcome is still the same: the resulting distribution of energy is more or less flat over the bandwidth of interest.

Equalizing the net system losses over frequency helps to eliminate ISI, a major cause of poor signal integrity. Without equalization, different frequencies of driven energy would encounter different losses. In practice, this means that different data patterns would likely pass through the system with different attenuations (a 1010101010... pattern would encounter high losses, while a 111110000... pattern has a lower effective frequency and bits after the first bit would encounter less loss). Different edges, resulting from reflections and constructive/destructive interference, would be generated, causing pattern-dependent jitter, and in turn generate reflections that would also encounter varying attenuation levels. In short, losses that are dramatically different with frequency will tend to compound negative signal integrity impacts such as ISI and jitter.

The mechanism of equalization for most computer data interfaces is to scale the driven voltage of the transmitter depending on the bit pattern being driven and the expected response of the system to it. A lower-loss system with significant reflections may show considerable "bouncing" of signals back and forth between driver and receiver. Therefore, the energy from a driven bit may affect subsequent bits several bit-cycles later. A lossy system with fewer discontinuities causing reflections may result in any driven bit affecting subsequent bits a few cycles later only. The relative length of time between the affected bits and the bit causing distorting reflections is called *channel memory*. By scaling a certain number of transmitted bits corresponding to the channel memory of the interface, the transmitted energy can be equalized to minimize ISI.

The most common industry implementation of equalization is the digital finite impulse response (FIR) filter shown in Figure 3.15. The incoming data stream is scaled depending on the coefficients supplied at each *tap* or summation point, with more taps corresponding to a longer channel memory requiring equalization. Properly calculated coefficients can eliminate much of a system's ISI, if an appropriate number of taps is available.

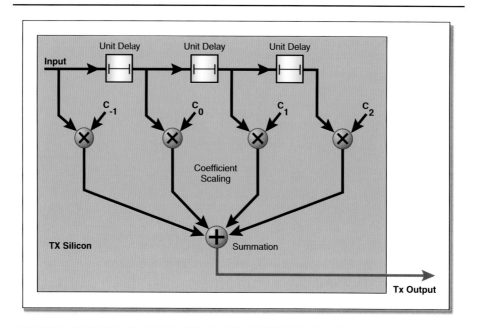

**Figure 3.15** Finite Impulse Response Structure

Simple, two-tap forms of equalization where the transmitter energy is increased at the higher frequencies may be called *pre-emphasis* in common industry usage. Reducing transmitter energy at the lower frequencies in a two-tap implementation is called *de-emphasis* in common industry usage.

The relative position of the taps in the timeline of a data stream is important, as the scaling of a driven bit and the bit immediately following tend to be strongest, with preceding and subsequent bits usually requiring less scaling. The tap that corresponds to the driven bit in a bit stream is called the cursor, while the pre- and post-cursors correspond to the taps, and therefore bits, immediately before and after the cursor in time. This relationship is shown in Figure 3.16.

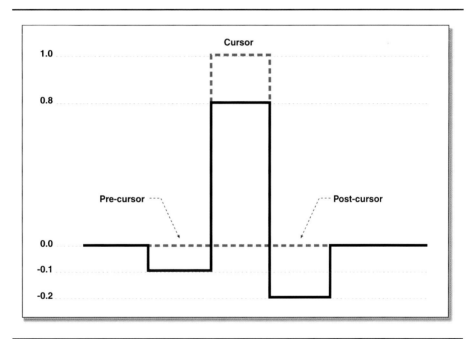

**Figure 3.16** Placement of Pre-cursor, Cursor, and Post-cursor in Transmitted Waveform

Figure 3.17 shows the response at the receiver from a pulse sent down a highly discontinuous line with no equalization assumed. Figure 3.18 shows the eye diagram that results from a bitstream on such a channel. Equalization applied to the transmitter, in this case four taps, increases and decreases selected areas of the pulse response, to make the received pulse more strongly resemble an attenuated pulse with no reflective impacts, as shown in Figure 3.19. The resulting eye is also shown in Figure 3.20, making clear the advantages to signal integrity of properly selected tap architectures and tap coefficients.

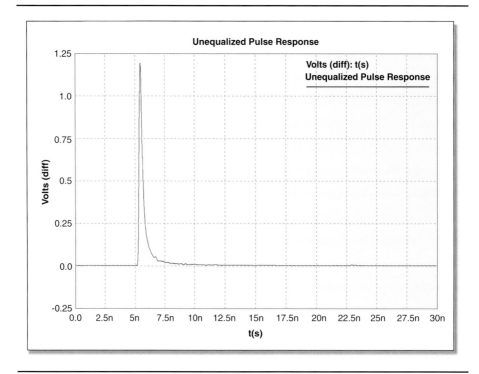

**Figure 3.17** Pulse Response of System with Unequalized Transmitter

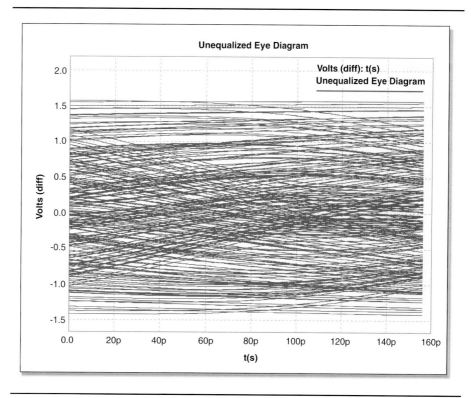

**Figure 3.18** Eye Diagram for System with Unequalized Transmitter

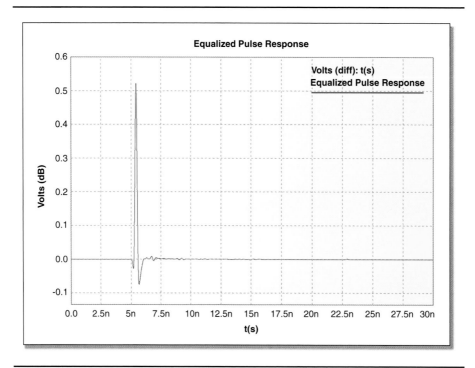

**Figure 3.19** Pulse Response of System with Equalized Transmitter

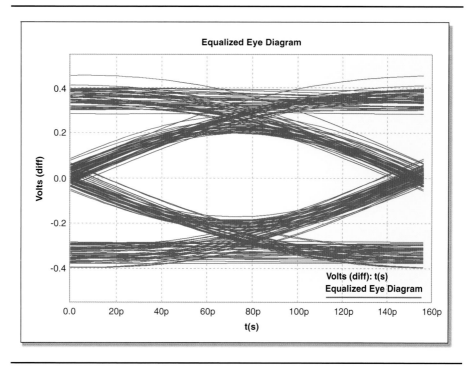

**Figure 3.20** Eye Diagram for System with Equalized Transmitter

For Intel QPI designs, the number of taps required depends on the platform and components involved. More complex topologies may have longer traces, more connectors, layer transitions, and the like and therefore may require more transmitter taps in order to properly compensate for losses and system ISI effects. Commonly, only two-tap (cursor and post-cursor) and four-tap (pre-cursor, cursor, first post-cursor, and second post-cursor) architectures are required and available for Intel QPI. Specific implementations of multi-tap transmitter designs are shown in Chapter 4.

## Receivers and Terminations

Intel QPI systems do not require external terminations, either for the data or clock signals. Both the transmitting and the receiving devices in an Intel QPI system contain terminations that automatically compensate to an 85-ohm differential (42.5-ohm single-ended) target.

As of this publication, transmitter equalization is the primary mechanism for controlling loss and ISI effects in available Intel QPI systems. Receiver designs are modeled as parallel resistor-capacitor circuits, to represent the impedance of the receiving I/O buffer presented to the system. More details on the modeling assumptions used here are given in Chapter 4. In some cases, designs and models for receiving devices may contain additional amplification circuits. However, these are usually fixed-gain "boosters," intended to provide some additional eye height margin at the decision point of the receiver circuit.

Note that today's Intel QPI platforms do not make use of adaptive equalization, as is the case with IEEE 802.3ap and other serial-differential interfaces. Adaptation is intended for devices that may undergo radical changes in their operating environments (such as substitution of a long cable for a short one with no other changes to the system), or for devices that cannot be configured a priori for the systems in which they will be used. Intel QPI systems are highly constrained, in that interconnect parameters, topology features, and lengths do not change once the system design is complete. The appropriate lifetime system equalization settings can therefore be calculated as the design is completed. Adaptation would introduce circuit complexity unnecessary for the Intel QPI environment at its current speeds.

## Connectors, Sockets, and Packages

Connectors for Intel QPI are most likely to be used in multiprocessor Intel Xeon® processor or Intel Itanium® processor designs. For example, a rack-mounted system may involve connecting 4, 8, or more processors and/or I/O hubs simultaneously through connectors to a backplane PCB.

Electrically, the ideal Intel QPI connector will be electrically invisible to the signals passing through it. Realistically, good connector designs will exhibit low losses, good impedance matching to the specification target (85 ohms) and low crosstalk between signals. Furthermore, some connector designs (for example, right-angle connectors) may introduce more skew into some signal paths than others, as the signals on the outer edge of the right-angle bend will have a longer distance to travel than the signals on the inner edge. While pair-to-pair skews (delays) may not be as critical to Intel QPI performance as within-pair skews, both should be controlled to within specification requirements, and connector designs should be checked for compliance.

Specifications for Intel QPI connector electrical design and for electrical measurements are available. Some suggestions as to good modeling practices for connectors are given in Chapter 4. Contact your Intel field representative for copies.

In contrast to connectors, most platform designs will feature at least one socket (any CPU components will most likely be socketed and the I/O hub may also be socketed in system validation designs). The signal integrity effects and therefore the principles of socket selection are the same as for Intel QPI interface connectors: signals should have minimal pair-to-pair crosstalk, minimal skews between signals within any pair and should exhibit the same impedance as the system target (85 ohms). Again, like the connector, the objective is to make the socket appear to be electrically invisible, neglecting signal propagation delays not constrained by the specification.

Package design parameters are under the control of the component provider, and are therefore beyond significant influence by the system designer. In general, however, the principles of package design match those of all other passive components in an Intel QPI system. Losses will be minimized, as will pair-to-pair skews and impedance mismatches. As with PCB designs, a tradeoff exists between the number of layers needed to successfully route signals from a package, and the number of layers in that package. More layers will increase costs and make referencing and impedance matching more difficult (for example, more vias will exist in each signal path).

Modeling recommendations for all these components are given in Chapter 4.

## Interconnect Traces and Breakouts

As with connectors, sockets, and packages, the impact of poor PCB trace layout on signal integrity phenomena can be severe. Further, the PCB trace parameters, such as geometry, length, and electrical parameters stemming from material properties are under more direct control of the system designer than any other part of the interface.

As with other portions of the channel, the major factors affected by the PCB trace layout are loss, crosstalk, and reflective effects from impedance mismatches. While traces can contribute to jitter by a phenomenon called *jitter amplification*, this effect is secondary to the jitter induced from impedance mismatches and frequency-dependent losses.

Though losses due to the trace as a conductor are certainly a factor, losses in the frequency bandwidth used by Intel QPI are primarily from material effects and can therefore be controlled through careful attention to stackup geometries, dielectric constants, dielectric loss tangents, and surface roughness. For any given stackup, making trace adjustments to cross-sectional geometry is the easiest way to control both conductor and dielectric losses. For the same dielectric thicknesses and materials, differential traces at lower impedances (for example, 85 ohms rather than 100 ohms) will have lower losses.

One major but often ignored set of relationships is that of humidity and temperature to dielectric loss. The dielectric material used in typical FR-4-based designs can absorb moisture, particularly as temperatures increase. This moisture increase will also tend to increase the capacity of the material to store energy, making the effective loss tangent of the material appear to increase. Standards for humidity and temperature conditions for server operation are defined by the American Society of Heating, Refrigerating, and Air-Conditioning Engineers (ASHRAE). As a rule of thumb, signal integrity analyses should assume loss tangents at or near the maximum of the specified range for the given material. If humidity and/or temperature data for the material is available, the extremes of environmental conditions should be assumed when assessing the dielectric constant and loss tangent of the material. For typical FR-4 (that is, without considering lead-free or halide-free materials), this will typically mean using a loss tangent of around 0.022.

The most significant physical parameter that can limit negative signal integrity impacts and is still under the control of the board designer is the trace routing length. Longer traces will increase trace loss, as the resistance of the trace and the surface area through which energy is absorbed by the dielectric are increased. In addition, longer routing of parallel signals will increase the crosstalk between those signals, from the same increase in coupled surface area. Merely routing short traces is not a risk-free solution, however. As noted above, extremely short channels may create resonances from energy reflecting between the driver and the receiver without attenuation from the channel.

Many different types of trace route may exist on the same Intel QPI interface on the same platform (for example, multiple stripline layers, mixed microstrip and stripline routing, and so on). Even a simple topology routed from processor to processor on only a single layer may involve two different geometries: one for the narrow trace widths and spacing permitted within the ballout of the processors ("breakout") and the wider widths and spacings available in the less-constrained open field between the device breakouts, as shown in Figure 3.21. This raises the risk of impedance mismatches and resulting reflections, leading to ISI. Each portion of a PCB route should be carefully designed so that impedance mismatches are minimized.

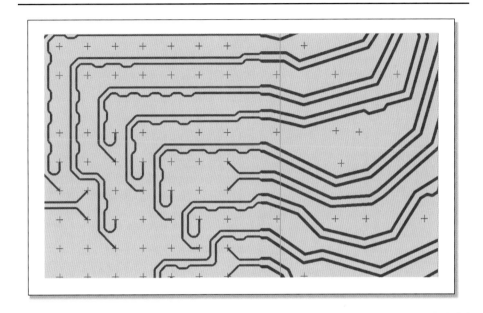

**Figure 3.21** Changes in Trace Width Due to Breakout from Component Region

Typically, Intel platform design guidelines include information on the impedance tolerances permitted for particular stackup geometries and routing layers. However, maintaining the PCB trace impedance targets across a high volume production run is left to the final manufacturer of the PCB. Unlike connectors and sockets, PCB traces may exhibit significant variation in physical and electrical properties in manufacturing. The statistical distributions for individual parameters in the board—trace width, dielectric height, dielectric constant, trace spacing for differential impedance and crosstalk, and so on—may not be available or controllable by the board designer. Because a particular impedance may be achieved through many potential trace and stackup geometries, as shown in Figure 3.22, the losses for a given impedance target range may vary significantly. Figure 3.23 shows a simulated example where, for an 85-ohm target trace pair, the manufacturing variations that give rise to different differential impedances create a 0.5-dB difference in insertion loss at 6.4 GHz, for a 10-inch trace segment.

How to estimate PCB parameter distributions for worst-case design is a problem not easily solved. For simulation, the most useful approach is to combine extremes of the given stackup parameters that result in worst-case impedances, crosstalks, and losses, based on one's target stackup and data from one's PCB suppliers. However, the extremes of all the stackup parameters are unlikely to occur simultaneously (if they did, the target impedance range would likely be exceeded).[6] As impedance is most easily controlled by limiting trace width, other stackup parameters should be allowed to vary to their full extremes, with trace width limitations used to maintain impedances within the target range. Other combinations, such as those resulting in worst-case extremes of loss, crosstalk and propagation delay, may be created to ensure complete simulation coverage. While worst-case extremes may result in conservative designs, failures due to manufacturing variations will be avoided.

---

6   Similarly, the nominal values within each stackup parameter range will likely not result in the nominal impedance or the nominal loss for the platform.

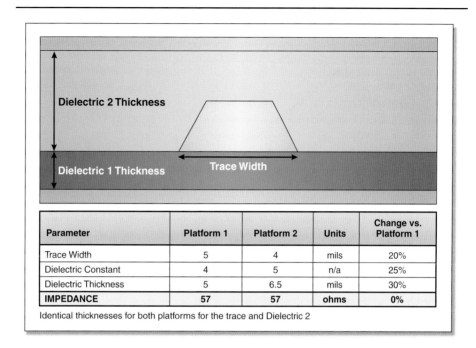

| Parameter | Platform 1 | Platform 2 | Units | Change vs. Platform 1 |
|---|---|---|---|---|
| Trace Width | 5 | 4 | mils | 20% |
| Dielectric Constant | 4 | 5 | n/a | 25% |
| Dielectric Thickness | 5 | 6.5 | mils | 30% |
| **IMPEDANCE** | **57** | **57** | **ohms** | **0%** |

Identical thicknesses for both platforms for the trace and Dielectric 2

**Figure 3.22** Variations in Stackup with Identical Impedance

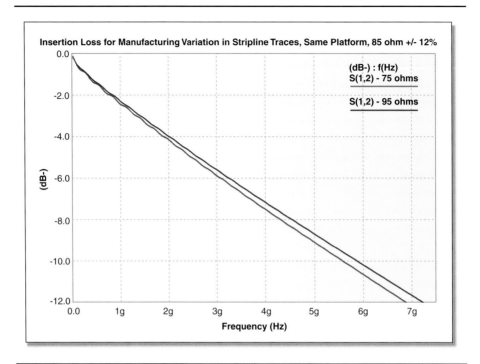

**Figure 3.23** Insertion Loss Changes with Manufacturing Variations

A relatively new concern to board designers is the impact of FR-4 fiber weave on the effective dielectric constant and loss tangent of the material. FR-4-based PCBs use dielectric layers made of a glass fabric covered in a resin epoxy, as shown in Figure 3.24. Materials with different resin ratios have different dielectric constants. More importantly, the routing of traces over the glass fabric results in the traces "seeing" different material properties between them and the reference plane, as the trace route passes either over a glass fiber bundle or over a gap between bundles. The bundles have electrical properties closer to pure glass, while the gaps more closely resemble the resin epoxy electrically. The trace single-ended impedance will then vary over the length of the route. Further, the differential impedance of the trace pair may also vary significantly if one trace in the pair passes over different bundle-epoxy changes than the other trace in the pair. This variation can cause skews in the signal and therefore jitter.

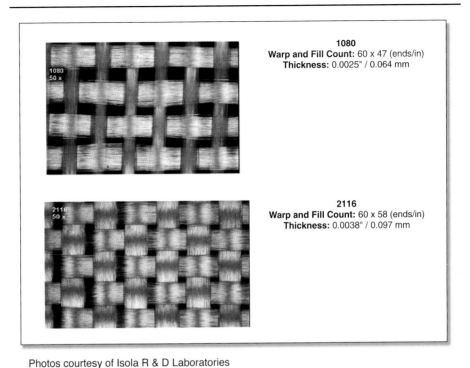

1080
**Warp and Fill Count:** 60 x 47 (ends/in)
**Thickness:** 0.0025" / 0.064 mm

2116
**Warp and Fill Count:** 60 x 58 (ends/in)
**Thickness:** 0.0038" / 0.097 mm

Photos courtesy of Isola R & D Laboratories

**Figure 3.24** Glass Fiber Densities for Different Dielectric Materials

Mitigation of fiber weave effects is best done by requiring regular bends or changes in direction of the routes. Between the bends, the route lengths are also limited. Alternately, the entire route may be placed at an angle relative to the edges of the board (assuming the fiber weave is aligned with the board edges), as shown in Figure 3.25. By preventing long trace routes aligned with the weave, the average chances are reduced of having a trace routed over glass bundles with its neighbor over epoxy.

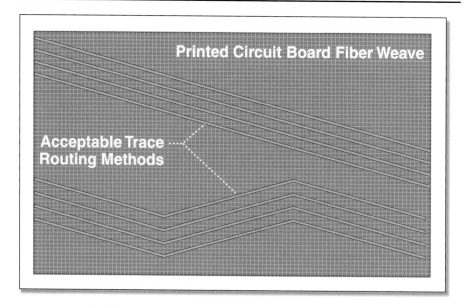

**Figure 3.25** Options for Avoiding Fiber Weave Impact

Additional details on modeling interconnect traces, particularly regarding causality and passivity, are given in Chapter 4. More specific routing rules for Intel QPI are provided in Chapter 6.

## Vias

For many lower-speed or lower-edge-rate applications, the contribution of vias to the overall electrical path of a signal is considered negligible. To that class of designs, the via had no influence on the received signal and could therefore be ignored. For Intel QPI, regardless of whether the via is used for a connector or for a layer transition, this approach is no longer adequate. The via introduces a more significant impedance discontinuity, and its reflective effects can have a negative impact on system performance.

The largest electrical effect of a via is the via "stub" or the portion of the via length that does not provide an electrical signal path between layers. For example, a via designed to connect the top layer to the middle layer of a PCB will likely extend through the entire board. The via barrel will form an unterminated but conductive region of metal. Signals of sufficiently high edge rate can enter and reflect within this region. Like a short trace, a via stub can cause reflections on high speed signals and therefore contribute to ISI.

The most advantageous system designs feature compensation for via stub effects. This can be through "backdrilling" where unused electrically conductive material has been removed from the via by a drill slightly larger than the diameter of the via. A similar approach, using microvias or blind vias, involves eliminating unused sections of a via by only drilling the PCB layers to be connected with vias, and then only before assembly of the full board. Alternately, stub effects can be reduced can be through inductive compensation, where additional PCB trace routing is used to add trace inductance that can negate the impact of the capacitance of the via.

In general, via stubs should be minimized wherever possible, particularly on designs with thicker PCBs. Intel platform design guidelines permit via stubs for some board designs and provide information on restrictions and compensation methods. As a rule of thumb, Intel QPI interfaces running at or below 6.4 GT/s require via compensation for any vias longer than 70 mils. However, this may vary depending on the routing length and other reflective effects in the system.

Overall, the Intel QPI specification treats all interconnect components as part of one end-to-end channel. No specific budgets are derived for vias, connectors, etc. within that channel. This provides great flexibility to individual system designers to establish a working solution space. This raises the importance of system analysis through simulation, as discussed in Chapter 4.

## Performance Budgeting: Eye Diagrams

The Intel QPI specification and associated documents (such as the model user's guides for individual platforms) use eye diagrams to describe the evaluation requirements for the interface. These permit simple pass-versus-fail characterization of a particular design. They also have the advantage of being easily applied both in laboratory and simulation contexts.

An eye diagram is simply a time-domain waveform showing voltage "wrapped" or plotted using a fixed, cyclical time period, rather than a time axis of increasing length. The time period is usually defined as the bit time or one-half the period of the signal. The period is, in turn, the reciprocal of the frequency (for illustrative purposes, eye diagrams are sometimes plotted showing two bit times side-by-side). An eye diagram is generated much the same way a manual typewriter's carriage moves when the carriage return key is pressed. The voltage is plotted from a particular time point until a bit time has been completed. The time axis is then reset to the leftmost starting point as the voltage plot continues. In this way, time-domain data of any duration is plotted in a space of fixed length.

The advantage of this approach is that the behavior per bit of the signal can easily be seen. The smallest and largest "eyes" or individual bits appear as part of the same visual image. The cumulative effect of noise on the timing and amplitude of a signal are easily perceived.

Eye requirements are defined in terms of width and height (often abbreviated as EW and EH, respectively). As shown in Figure 3.26, the eye height is usually defined for a particular time within the eye. The eye width is the minimum time between crossing points, where rising and falling edges achieve the same voltage value. Defining a minimum eye diagram or eye template for the interface to satisfy effectively defines the minimum signal amplitude and maximum jitter the receiver can withstand.

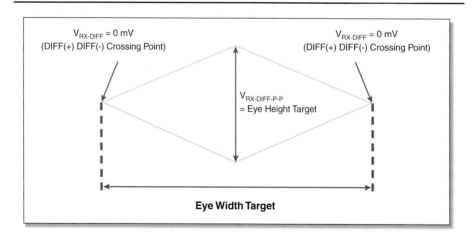

**Figure 3.26** Example Eye Mask for Intel® QuickPath Interconnect

## Bit Error Rate (BER)

Many serial-differential interfaces also define a BER (bit error rate or bit error ratio) requirement to observe. This value defines the maximum number of errors or indeterminate bit states permitted to occur for a given number of transmitted bits. Unlike earlier technologies, the protocols behind these newer interfaces include error recovery, which allows the fixed number of errors defined by the BER without causing system failure.

The Intel QPI BER is 1 error in every $10^{14}$ bits (a number of specific validation test requirements are also defined for 1 error in every $10^9$ and $10^{12}$ bits, which will be discussed in Chapter 6). For simulation purposes, the eye diagrams provided in the model user's guide for particular combinations of components correspond to this target BER.

# Chapter 4

# Time and Frequency Domain Modeling and Simulation

**A**nalysis of an Intel® QuickPath Interconnect (Intel QPI) system may involve creating models and performing simulations in either the time or frequency domain or both. The following sections highlight methods for model creation in either domain, plus areas of concern in both.

## Linear and Time-Invariant Systems

Many high-speed serial-differential systems today are being designed in the digital arena using methods popular in the radiofrequency and microwave domains for many years. A major assumption underlying the recommended method for simulating the Intel QPI interface is that the simulation models, and the components they represent, are *linear and time-invariant* (LTI).

Linearity simply means that a system satisfies both *scaling* and *superposition*. In scaling, the inputs to a system may be multiplied by a numeric quantity and a proportional change in the output will occur. In superposition, multiple inputs combine through summation to form the output. One can see that a simple resistor network easily satisfies both scaling and superposition. If the network has a single input and single output, increasing the input by a factor of ten results in a tenfold increase in the output. Similarly, a resistor network with multiple inputs has an output current that is the sum of all the input currents (assuming consistent directions and signs). By analogous thinking, the voltages and currents of a diode have a nonlinear relationship, because the current through the diode does not always change in direct proportion to the voltage across it, for all regions of operation.

Time-invariance refers to the relationship between the system's behavior and the times at which inputs and outputs change. If the relationship between the inputs and outputs of the system is unrelated to time, as would be true with the resistor network, the system is time-invariant. A signal sent today through the network would produce an output identical to that from a signal sent yesterday or tomorrow. A device with memory, by contrast, is not necessarily time-invariant. A signal sent today may result in an output different than that sent tomorrow or yesterday, depending on the previous state of the system.

An LTI system combines both linearity and time-invariance, so that a signal sent through such a system always results in the same output, no matter when the input is provided. Similarly, the output is a summation of all inputs, with predictable relationships between the magnitude of the inputs and the magnitude of the output.

In an analog simulation context, the treatment of LTI and non-LTI systems confers a strong advantage to LTI designs. If LTI conditions are satisfied, the voltage and current state of the system can be determined by a simulation engine through simple matrix manipulation for any time point. For non-LTI systems, the state of the system will be different for different time points, with a nonlinear relationship to the system's state at previous times. An iterative, time-step–based approach is needed to converge on the voltages and currents at particular times, taking initial conditions into account.

The value of an LTI system in terms of analysis should now be clear. For an LTI system, time-step–based analog analysis is not necessary beyond the work needed to obtain the initial system response.

Assuming a system has been operating for some time and will continue to do so, each bit driven onto the bus falls previous to a bit and subsequent to another bit. A pre-cursor for one sequence may be the post-cursor (first, second, third, and so on) for an earlier one. So long as the system characteristics do not change with time, individual bit streams do not have to be analyzed separately. Instead, a single pulse response can be generated for the entire system and then the response can be convolved with the bit-time for the interface. By superposition, individual responses for pre-cursor, cursor, and post-cursor bits driven down the same interconnect can be summed to form the composite response of the interface to any data pattern. The characterized response of the system therefore can be manipulated mathematically very quickly to see the effects of any data pattern. Through scaling and superposition, a driven signal can be combined with reflected signal energy to produce a final waveform showing the impact of impedance discontinuities and loss, for any probing point in the system.

Intel's tools, models, and methods, including peak distortion analysis (PDA) as described later in this chapter, rely on the LTI assumption to help speed analysis of complex systems.

## Time-Domain Modeling

The recommended method for analyzing the signal integrity of Intel QuickPath Interconnect systems involves bitstream and pulse response simulation in the time domain. Models generated for all parts of the system interconnect should therefore be applicable to time-domain simulations. For most purposes, W-element (described below) and SPICE equivalent circuit models are sufficient to represent the time-domain behavior of all typical system components.

Time-domain modeling of Intel QuickPath Interconnect topologies involves separating the topology into parts and capturing the most important effects of each part in a system model that can be easily and quickly simulated. Key parts of the topology include:

- transmitters
- receivers
- interconnects

Each of these is described in detail in the following sections.

### Transmitter Modeling

Time-domain modeling of Intel QuickPath Interconnect drivers involves three key areas:

- current sources, switches, and output impedance
- equalizers
- stimulus patterns and filtering

In general, the driver design used for Intel QuickPath Interconnect is highly similar to that used for PCI Express[†], Serial ATA, the Universal Serial Bus (USB) and other serial-differential drivers used in computing platforms. At a simplified level, the interfaces can be represented as an always-on current source[1], as shown in Figure 4.1. Logical 0 and 1 values are driven by activating or deactivating switches, connected between the current source and the driver pads, in a complementary manner. Resistive terminations at each pad convert the driven current into a voltage at the pad when the associated switch is closed.

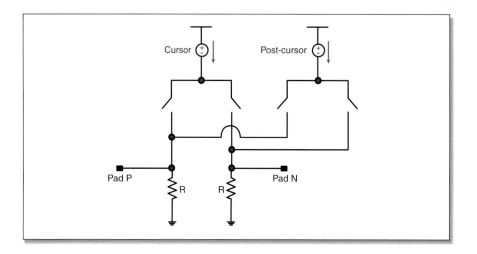

**Figure 4.1**    A Simple Transmitter

In reality, each switch is in fact a single transistor or group of transistors with a nonzero "on" resistance (Ron) or impedance, operating either off or in the transistors' linear region. The output terminations also have finite impedance and are typically designed as banks of parallel resistors in series with transistors, to allow automatic compensation of their combined impedance to some target. The current source usually consists of one or more control transistors, biased to operate in saturation, so that their current output is relatively unchanged by voltage variations.

---

1    Driver designs based on voltage sources may also be used. However, in practice, this may make balancing edge rates between the two halves of the differential pair more difficult across process, voltage, and temperature variations.

Driver impedance can vary over switch state and voltage for a variety of reasons. First, the current source's impedance is not infinite. Second, using transistors or transistors in series with resistances for control does not ensure constant resistance over voltage. Finally, state-of-the-art CMOS processes have a small saturation range relative to the supply voltage used. As a result, voltage variations may cause the current source driver to move out of the saturation region and therefore away from constant-current behavior.

This entire circuit can be modeled with very few components using the netlisting syntax of any commercial SPICE program. More realistic models will represent the current source as ideal, but with parallel resistance and capacitance to provide realistic impedance, as shown in Figure 4.2. Similarly, the output pad's capacitance will be included in the model in parallel with the compensated termination resistors, and the switches themselves can be represented as resistors with very high off impedances and very low on impedances. A capacitor at the switch input (not shown) may be added to ensure realistic transitions on the switches, to mimic driver input from the pre-driver.

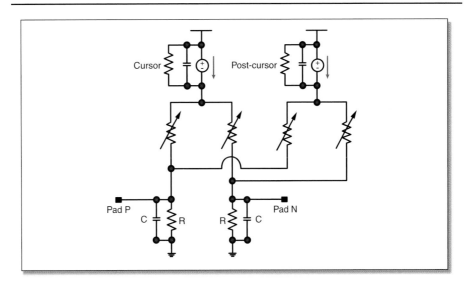

**Figure 4.2**   Detailed Transmitter Model

As noted above, the essential requirement of fast serial-differential system analysis is that the system be LTI[2]. One can see that, if accurate to the physical design, the circuit shown in Figure 4.2 is linear and time-invariant with respect to the output pads so long as the buffer does not operate at voltages large enough to trigger ESD diode behaviors or trigger the parasitic diode behaviors of the driver transistors.

Time-domain modeling is usually performed using analog simulation engines such as those present in commercial SPICE design software. As a result, the input stimulus pattern for the driver switches must be provided in an analog format with finite edges, rather than the infinite edges of the perfect 0 and 1 levels in a digital simulator (for example, using VHDL or Verilog). To properly represent this in designs for Intel QPI, voltage limiters and a filter are added to the driver model, as shown in Figure 4.3, so that analog voltage sources driving between 0 and 1 V DC may be used to represent the data pattern provided by the transmitter's logic core. The voltage limiters help model the output swings associated with device variations in process, voltage, and temperature associated with silicon high-volume manufacturing. The filter, usually Bessel, helps to remove high frequency distortions present in the analog bit stream that would not be present at the output of a realistic pre-driver design.

---

2   Most realistic systems will include some degree of nonlinear or time-dependent behavior. These effects may be accounted for through simulation of data patterns rather than pulse response, or through adjustment of eye diagrams and other evaluation criteria.

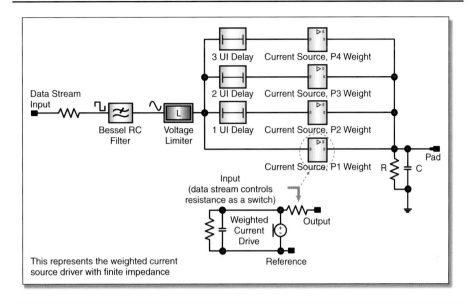

**Figure 4.3** Complete Transmitter Model

Unlike PCI Express, Intel QPI 1.0 does not use an encoding scheme like 8b/10b or 64b/66b. The stimulus pattern into the buffer may therefore cover any frequency or switching rate. This stimulus pattern should incorporate any scrambling, however.

The final component necessary to model an Intel QPI design is the equalizer. As noted in earlier chapters, Intel QPI, like PCI Express, Serial ATA, and other serial-differential interfaces, uses equalization (also called pre-emphasis or de-emphasis, depending on context[3]) to smooth the frequency-domain losses of the system across the target bandwidth, and therefore reduce the inter-symbol interference (ISI) and resulting jitter that can result. Equalization enables tuning of output drive strengths based on the data pattern to be driven, so that reflections from impedance discontinuities can be compensated with lower or even negative voltages.

---

3   Pre-emphasis implies that the response of the system across its bandwidth (frequency range of interest) is flattened by boosting the driver output energy in the higher frequencies, to compensate for high-frequency channel losses. De-emphasis implies that the response is flattened by reducing the driver output energy in the lower frequencies, matching the losses seen in the higher range. In either case, the frequency response is flattened, reducing inter-symbol interference (ISI).

Typical serial-differential designs may use only two taps or current sources to drive the output signal and compensate for ISI. More complex systems, particularly backplane-style designs with multiple connectors and media impedances and loss characteristics, may require additional taps to help compensate for the more complex reflective environment and corresponding channel memory or reflection duration. Each tap may be modeled as an additional current source, with its own associated additional components for realistic impedance.

Taps are commonly named in terms of the cursor, or actual pulse sent down the interconnect to the receiver by the driver. The cursor is the block of time or unit interval (UI) in a time-domain pulse corresponding to the actual bit to be transmitted. The term cursor can also refer to the coefficient to be applied for that particular block of time. Similarly, the pre-cursor is the block of time or UI in a pulse train immediately before the bit to be transmitted. The first post-cursor is the block of time or UI immediately after the transmitted bit. Each coefficient is signed, though the cursor is usually positive and the first post-cursor usually negative. In device specifications, the absolute values of tap coefficients are usually required to sum to 1.0.[4] A useful way to think about coefficients is to imagine them as the "area under the curve" of the time-domain waveform itself. The area corresponds to the transmitted energy of a full-voltage-swing bit.

By the theory of PDA, the pre-cursor, cursor, and post-cursor portions of a particular bit are affected by the cursor and post-cursor portions of the previous bit, respectively. By superposition, these can be added to find the total high and low voltages for each respective bit or UI. Tuning of the coefficients can preserve a minimum eye opening once the channel memory and superimposed bit voltages are taken into account.

Figure 4.4 shows the relationship of pre-cursor and first-post-cursor to a particular cursor in a pulse response for a three-tap design.

---

4   Coefficients that sum to less than zero would imply that the waveform is scaled to some fraction of a full-swing signal bit. Similarly, coefficients that sum to more than 1.0 would imply amplification.

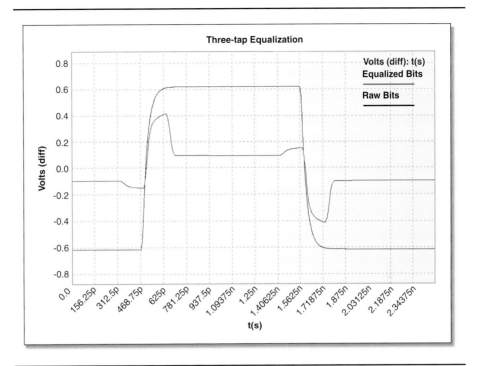

**Figure 4.4**    Pre-cursor, Cursor, and Post-cursor Equalization

Different Intel components may implement tap programming differently. Some devices may require explicit programming of the cursor tap, while others may calculate a cursor equalization coefficient based upon the other equalization values (first post-cursor, pre-cursor if any, and so on). Consult the device firmware guide or BIOS specification for details on translating tap coefficients to BIOS register settings for a specific component.

To ensure relatively easy analysis of a complex driver design, the model must include parameterized values for driver impedance (as resistance and capacitance), the output strength of each current source, the voltage swing expected at the output plus any pre-driver controls (such as stimulus patterns edge rates). The output current strength of each tap may be set according to the optimum equalization coefficients necessary to reduce or remove system ISI. Therefore, the model format used to represent the driver must support variable controls on all of these components. A behavioral representation of the buffer ensures high simulation speed. Formats such as Verilog-A and non-transistor behavioral SPICE usually provide a good balance between simulation speed, simulator cost, and simplicity of model structure. Verilog-AMS and VHDL-AMS are less attractive as formats due to the higher costs of the engines that support them, while traditional table-driven IBIS (version 4.0 and below) requires a separate model for each variable setting, raising the complexity of system analysis over high-volume variation.

In general, the buffer used to model Intel QPI is highly similar to those used to model PCI Express (5 GT/s) on server platforms. The main difference is that in PCI Express, the buffer equalization is limited to one of only two or three settings (off, 3.5 dB or 6 dB). This is equivalent to a two-tap equalization design in Intel QPI, with a cursor, no pre-cursor and a single post-cursor.

A few other considerations should be taken into account for the specific implementation of Intel QPI links. First, no energy is added by the tap scaling used by the transmitter. In other words, the total energy driven by an unequalized and an equalized transmitter should be the same. Only the distribution of energy changes with equalization, depending on the coefficients themselves. An easy check to ensure that correct taps are being used is to add up the absolute values of all the tap decimal coefficients. These should always add up to 1.0, assuming appropriate precisions are used. Intel tools and models enforce this automatically. For example, tap values of −0.05, 0.8, −0.15 for pre-cursor, cursor and post-cursor respectively would be added together as |-0.05|+|0.8|+|-0.15| to sum to 1.0.

Intel tools can provide the optimum taps for any particular pulse response provided, assuming the bit time, number of taps desired, and other information are also supplied. These taps are provided as decimal coefficients, and must be converted to hexadecimal values before programming them into a platform's BIOS. The programming assumptions and procedure will differ depending on the component involved. Consult your component BIOS specifications or Intel field representative for details.

## Receiver Modeling

The platform topologies of today's Intel QPI–based systems, even in the Expandable (EX) and Mission Critical (MC) market segments, are not usually so complicated as to require configurable receiver equalization for adequate performance (see Chapter 3 for a discussion of equalization). Transmit equalization with four or fewer taps is usually sufficient to achieve Intel QPI bit error rate targets. As a result, the receiver designs and corresponding models are simple in comparison to the drivers.

As shown in Figure 4.5, the Intel QPI receiver may be modeled as a simple resistor in parallel with a capacitor at each pad of the differential buffer. The receiver itself consists of a termination, compensated automatically as in the case of the driver. As in any buffer, the device pad has capacitance as does the metal interconnect between the pad and other receiver components. This capacitance, like the compensated resistance, will vary slightly depending on process, voltage, and temperature and should therefore be parameterized in the model. As the Intel QPI interface model user's guides are written from the perspective of the at-pad behavior of the incoming signals, the comparator used to remove common-mode effects and provide an input signal to the logic core of the receiver is not modeled. As a result, an R-C circuit is more than adequate to represent the receiver buffer across the target bandwidth. In more complex MC or EX systems, an amplifier may be part of the circuit, as shown in Figure 4.6, after the R-C circuit but before the comparator. The amplifier itself is typically represented as a fixed frequency-dependent table of voltages, to accurately represent the response of the amplifier over the target interface bandwidth.

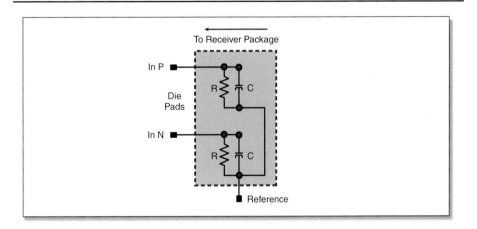

**Figure 4.5**    Receiver Buffer

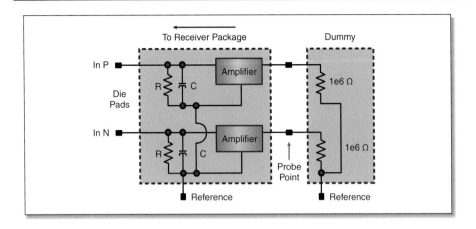

**Figure 4.6**  Receiver with Amplification

## Interconnect Component Modeling

The only active devices involved in Intel QuickPath Interconnect links are the driver and the receiver. The rest of the links consist of the device packages, the printed circuit board (PCB) traces, component sockets, the vias at layer transitions, and any connectors between boards or to probing structures.

For time-domain signal integrity simulation purposes, these interconnects can be modeled in several ways, including:

■ tabular RLGC matrices for W-elements

■ SPICE netlists of R, L, C components plus current and voltage sources

Interconnects may also be modeled using S-parameters, with caution, as described in the section "Frequency-Domain Modeling."

Fundamentally, any models representing interconnects in an Intel QuickPath Interconnect system design must satisfy two requirements:

■ passivity

■ causality

*Passivity* simply means that the component model does not exhibit any gain or power amplification. While reflections may cause voltages to appear to increase due to constructive interference, the overall output power of the system must be equal to or less than the power input of the system, because the interconnects exhibit dissipative losses (including skin effect, dielectric loss, radiation, and dispersion).

*Causality* refers to the relation of cause and effect in time; cause must precede effect as time passes. Some modeling techniques may result in models where effects, such as voltage changes, occur in time before the events that caused them. This is a violation of basic physics and must be eliminated from any models used for Intel QuickPath Interconnect analyses, particularly when PDA is used.

Typically, all interconnect models are best extracted from a field solver. This simulation tool analyzes the distribution of electric and magnetic fields in the interconnect, across two or three dimensions. The non-tabular RLGC matrix-based W-element is the most common two-dimensional model for interconnects in industry today.

RLGC matrix models of traces are ground-reduced representations of the self- and mutual inductance (L), and capacitance (C) per unit length of a single interconnect path or a group of paths. Losses, in the form of DC and frequency-dependent resistance (R) and conductance (G), may also be included. The interconnect is assumed to vary in its electrical behavior only with length (in other words, because the RLGC matrices are two-dimensional, they do not model changes in cross-sectional geometry within a given length segment). Because symmetry of the coupling effects is assumed from one end of the model to the other, only the diagonal and either the lower- or upper-half of the matrix data is traditionally included in the model data.

The most common format for RLGC W-elements in industry includes separate matrices for L, C, R, and G, with R and G broken further into DC and AC matrices, for a total of six matrices per model. The inductance and resistance matrices refer to the conductors of a transmission line system, while the capacitance and conductance matrices refer to the dielectric around the conductors. The typical RLGC matrix form assumes the telegrapher's equations apply and that both inductance and capacitance do not vary with frequency. The typical RLGC matrix form also assumes the following relationship between resistance and conductance matrices:

$$R(f) = Ro + Rs * \sqrt{f}$$
$$G(f) = Go + Gd * f$$

While reasonable for low-frequency interconnects, these equations can predict behaviors that violate basic physical relationships in systems operating at higher frequencies (from switching or edge rates). The *tabular* form of RLGC matrix-based W-elements makes the frequency dependence of R, L, G, and C components explicit, ensuring that an engine using a properly generated model will follow basic physical laws. The tabular RLGC data format is strongly recommended for multi-gigahertz digital system simulation.

A weakness of the W-element approach is its representation of coupling. The W-element does not capture coupling outside of the 2-D plane in which the field solver captured the model data. This means that, for example, the coupling between a wire at 1 inch along its length and at 1 inch along a neighboring wire will be captured, but not at 1 inch and 1.1 inch, respectively. These effects may be either included in an overall eye diagram budget or extracted through 3-D field solver analysis.

*PCB Trace Effects*

As noted in Chapter 3, the routing between components in an Intel QPI system may not be simple. Even for designs without connectors, traces may be routed in the "escape" regions under or around the components with smaller widths in order to accommodate the increased density in those areas. The trace impedances of the escape or "breakout" regions will of course be different than those for the main or open-field routing used for the majority of the trace length. Furthermore, layer transitions may mean that multiple trace designs (microstrip and stripline, or stripline on layers with differing distances to reference planes) may be used on a single connection between a driver and receiver. These separate sections should be modeled separately in order to accurately capture potential sources of ISI.

Trace models must also reflect the manufacturing variations expected on the PCB once in high volume production. Intel platform design guidelines (PDGs) specify the impedance variations expected for each interface on each layer of the given stackup. Consideration should be given not merely to impedance but also to loss and other effects when generating trace models for these manufacturing corners. Among the variations to include in a comprehensive study are operating temperature and humidity for the systems, and the effective dielectric constants and loss tangents of the PCB due these environmental effects.

PCB traces routed in proximity to one another and sharing endpoints lend themselves well to modeling using RLGC matrices. However, as with the coupling problem noted above, the W-element format assumes that all lines within it are exactly the same length. In actual board layouts, mismatches in trace length will occur and analysis of them may be of interest. While additional single-ended (uncoupled) W-element segments may be added to a particular line to show a mismatch, this approach excludes the coupling outside of the 2-D plane, just as explained above. For simulation purposes, trace analyses should be conducted using more sophisticated techniques (such as 3-D field solvers) to assess the impact of mismatches. In the case of Intel QPI, mismatches are budgeted in the eye templates used for system analysis, and are accounted for in the PDG.

The fiber weave of the glass portion of the PCB can have a large impact on the effective dielectric "seen" by traces within any given trace pair. This effect cannot be easily compensated for in system simulation. A full 3-D field solver can analyze the signal interactions with areas of glass and epoxy with precision, but only if detailed information is available on the material properties of each component of the dielectric. Additionally, the exact arrangement of the fibers in the weave relative to the traces must be known in order for such an approach based on a 3-D field solver to succeed.

A more realistic approach to the fiber weave effect is to assume a homogenous dielectric with worst-case electrical parameters, and take steps outside of simulation to account for and minimize its impact. For Intel platforms, specific routing guidelines are given to mitigate the effect of fiber weave in the PCB, and simulations are run to analyze margins for the system assuming these routing guidelines have been already applied.

A final effect to consider when modeling and simulating PCB traces is conductor surface roughness. Most advanced models of conductor losses include the skin effect, where the effective volume of metal through which signals pass is reduced. As frequencies increase, the signal migrates to a smaller portion of the outer dimensions of the conductor, making its effective resistance increase. A simple calculation can provide the skin depth, or distance into the metal that the signal penetrates.

For manufacturing, the metal surface of the foil used in PCB traces is roughened in order to strengthen its adhesive properties and ensure it is strongly anchored to the dielectric material around it. The profile of the trace then less resembles a smooth rectangle than a collection of bumps and jagged edges. With the increase in switching frequencies and edge rates in today's high-speed interfaces, the skin depth of PCB traces used for these interfaces may be on the order of the copper surface roughness contour features (the bumps and jagged edges). An updated model is therefore needed to ensure that surface roughness is properly taken into account when analyzing conductor loss.

Intel provides tools to convert field solver nontabular RLGC matrix output into a guaranteed-causal tabular model, with accurate conductor surface roughness impact, for use in Intel QuickPath Interconnect simulations.

### Packages and Sockets

In general, both the transmitter and receiver packages are modeled using a combination of W-elements (for the package substrate, which is highly similar to a PCB) and SPICE equivalent models (for the vias and package balls, which may not behave well for modeling using distributed 2-D techniques). These packages are supplied by the vendor and cannot usually be customized by the system designer. In most cases, variations in package impedance and trace lengths have been modeled. These can be included in system simulations through the use of design-specific models or parameterized controls.

In Intel QuickPath Interconnect system designs, processors are usually socketed components, while the I/O hub (IOH) is soldered directly to the PCB. As a result, the model sets provided by Intel to represent Intel QPI systems include the processor socket within the processor component package model. The socket is modeled in a similar fashion to the package.

### Connectors

Connectors for Intel QPI are most likely to be used in multiprocessor Intel Xeon® processor or Intel Itanium® processor designs. For example, a rack-mounted system may involve connecting four, eight or more processors and/or I/O hubs simultaneously through connectors to a backplane PCB.

Electrically, an Intel QPI connector must exhibit low losses, good impedance matching to the specification target (85 ohms) and low crosstalk between signals. Furthermore, some connector designs (for example, right-angle connectors) may introduce more skew into some signal paths than others, due to the signals on the outer edge of the right-angle bend having a longer distance to travel than the signals on the inner edge. While pair-to-pair skews (delays) may not be as critical to Intel QPI performance as within-pair skews, both should be controlled to within specification requirements, and connector designs should be checked for compliance.

Before simulation, users should consider tradeoffs between connector model precision and simulation time. Rational function approximation (RFA) is a good method for extracting via and connector modeling information into a SPICE equivalent circuit format from S-parameter data. In this process, the S-parameter response is fit to a polynomial equation, and this equation converted to an equivalent SPICE circuit using discrete resistors, capacitors, inductors, and sources. However, the size of the model is directly proportional to the precision (number of poles and zeros) included in it. Larger models will slow simulation time considerably. In many cases, users may find W-elements for connector models a more practical alternative. However, note that W-elements, not being 3-D models, may be optimistic in terms of the amount of crosstalk included. Crosstalk may be therefore budgeted through an adjustment to receiver eyes.

In some cases, time-domain simulation may be possible by directly using frequency-domain models (for example, S-parameter models for interconnects used in a time-domain SPICE engine). While apparently convenient, errors may result if the models used do not cover a bandwidth that is wide enough or involves a low enough starting frequency. In general, for Intel QuickPath Interconnect simulations, frequency-domain data should extend to DC or as near to it as possible, should use a bandwidth of approximately 100 GHz and should include finely spaced data points. While seemingly excessive relative to today's measurement capabilities, this ensures that the data is properly processed mathematically by simulation tools. A linearly spaced S-parameter set of 10,000 points is not unreasonable to ensure good time-domain response.

Similarly, some tools exist to extract time-domain SPICE models from S-parameter data, through methods such as RFA. While reasonable for connectors and vias, use of this technique for transmission lines may result in time-domain models that are not passive and/or causal, or may not scale with length as time-domain models such as RLGC matrices do. Further, the order of the function approximating the frequency response data is directly related to the size and complexity of the resulting time-domain circuit model. Larger simulation models will likely slow down simulation in the time domain. Users should exercise great caution in performing these kinds of model extractions. Generally, an order of 60 for connector models is reasonable, but the impact to simulation time may be significant and should be considered when creating the model.

Connector electrical, measurement, and modeling recommendations are available from Intel field representatives.

### Vias

Conceptually, the modeling approach for vias is highly similar to that used for connectors. Any model used to represent a via should include coupling effects to other vias and PCB features nearby. The model must also correctly model the parasitic capacitance of the via. The energy dissipation loss through the via is likely to be quite small, but the via's length may still be significant relative to the edge rates driven through it. Accordingly, the via may resemble a transmission line and so must be treated accordingly when representing its impedance in a model. Stubs resulting from an electrically long but unconnected portion of via will cause reflections at higher frequencies. To properly capture ISI in the overall system, via models should usually consist of more than lumped capacitances.

Extraction of via models using rational function approximation may not involve as many tradeoffs between simulation time and accuracy as may be true of a connector. In most cases, an extracted model of order 25 would be more than adequate. The bandwidth for a via model should be similar to that used for any connectors in the same system.

## Time-Domain Analysis

Analyses of Intel QuickPath Interconnect links focus on waveforms produced by time-domain SPICE simulations. Driver, receiver, and interconnect models are combined into a realistic netlist. The driver is stimulated with a pulse or bit stream and the output waveform is generated at the receiver pads. Post-processing on this waveform is performed using Intel tools to produce an eye diagram and, optionally, a worst-case bit pattern.

Some key features of the time-domain simulation and post-processing are described in the following sections.

### Analysis Types

Two kinds of time-domain analysis are supported by Intel QuickPath Interconnect models supplied by Intel. The first is bitstream, where a pattern of 0- and 1-valued bits is provided to the driver as input stimuli. The bit pattern may be of arbitrary length and may be user-defined, or it may be generated as the result of post-processing of other waveforms.

The other kind of analysis is peak distortion analysis (PDA), which relies on a single pulse or bit being driven by the transmitter down an otherwise quiet pair on the interface. This pulse, lasting only a single UI in duration, is sufficient in LTI systems to characterize the entire network in terms of reflections if the receiver is monitored until all reflections have died away, as shown in Figure 4.7. A process of convolution is used to add up the pulse and its reflections to establish the lowest voltage for a logical 1 and the highest voltage for a logical 0 possible on the interface using that topology. A worst-case eye diagram can then be plotted for the interface. Intel QuickPath Interconnect eye masks provided for simulation analysis assume PDA techniques. Note that the PDA eye masks provided correspond to only the interface or platform's target bit error ratio (BER). These masks should not be used to derive any other BERs or other performance metrics for the interface.

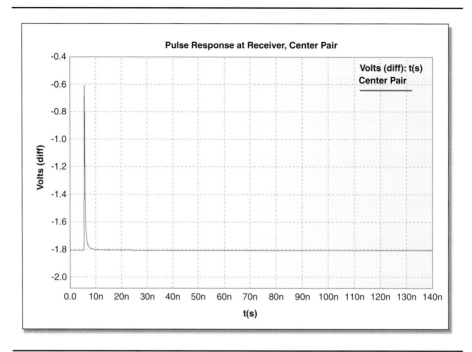

**Figure 4.7**  Pulse Response at Receiver

Note that the decks, or simulation netlists, provided by Intel and required for simulation, use three differential pairs (six signals) total. For PDA, the outer or "aggressor" pairs remain unstimulated and quiescent for simulation. They serve to illustrate crosstalk effects due to electromagnetic coupling between the traces on the PCBs and packages, plus in any connector structures, as shown in Figure 4.8. The center or victim pair is driven by the single pulse. In bitstream analysis, all three pairs may use different stimulus patterns.

Details on the mathematics behind PDA are provided in documents listed in the References section.

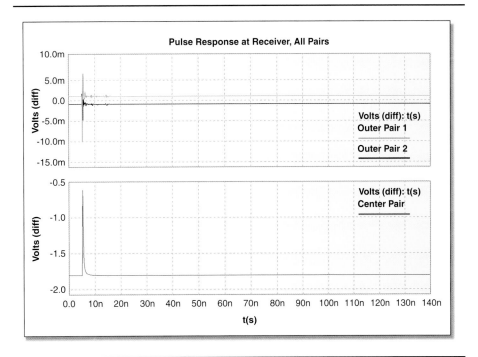

**Figure 4.8**  Crosstalk and Aggressor Pulse Responses at the Receiver

## ISI and Crosstalk

Inter-symbol interference (ISI) is generally included in time-domain simulation by its very nature: a simulation of a given duration with reasonably accurate models will include any ISI effects through that point in time. As a result, users should take care to simulate long enough, and with correct bit patterns, to cover the worst-case ISI behavior of the system. Similarly, to cover the worst-case ISI effects, the worst combinations of impedance discontinuities on the interface should be included in any study of a particular topology. Intel tools provide worst-case bit patterns for any given topology and, therefore, the proper duration for simulation for any given worst-case ISI effects,

As noted above, the topologies supplied by Intel as examples of Intel QuickPath Interconnect layout involve three differential pairs. The three pairs include crosstalk effects on the package as well as the PCB traces and any connector or via structures on the board, through modeling of electromagnetic coupling[5]. Because crosstalk is a major contributor to voltage reduction of a worst-case 1 and voltage boosting of worst-case 0 portions of an eye diagram, this three-pair format should be followed for extraction of any customer board topologies to be simulated.

Figure 4.8 shows the impact of crosstalk from the center pair of a simple three-pair system on the outer pairs. As crosstalk effects can have a significant impact on system margins and performance, careful routing and analysis of resulting crosstalk are required to ensure robust Intel QPI system design.

While crosstalk is critical, a key consideration is whether the simulation includes in-phase or all-phase crosstalk effects. In-phase crosstalk assumes that any coupling effects occur such that aggressor signal crosstalk edges are aligned with signal and/or clock edges on the victim signal. This means that edges on the victim are affected primarily by edge-related phenomena on the aggressors. Similarly, the settled high or low logic levels of the victim are affected by settling effects on the aggressors. The main advantage of in-phase crosstalk is its relative simplicity to set up—any analysis need only include the limited number of simulation cases and permutations where aggressor crosstalk is aligned with victim switching.

*All-phase crosstalk,* by contrast, makes no assumption regarding where in time on a victim signal the aggressors' impacts may be "felt." Crosstalk may therefore be considered when victim and aggressor edges are aligned or are offset by any fraction of a period (for example, the aggressors may switch when the victim is settling, in the middle of a particular bit, between edges). This can occur if aggressors and victim use an aligned stimulus pattern at their drivers, but use dissimilar routing that results in skewed arrival times at their respective receivers.

The disadvantages of in-phase versus all-phase crosstalk should now be clear. In-phase crosstalk, though computationally easier, may exclude cases where a worst-case logical one signal (lowest voltage) or a worst-case logical zero signal (highest voltage) occurs due to crosstalk of ringing effects from aggressors to victim. All-phase crosstalk can detect these true worst-case combinations of aggressor and victim alignment. However, this is computationally intense, involving many more permutations of aggressor and victim switching. Additionally, the worst-case all-phase crosstalk found

---

5   Note that crosstalk may only include effects within a pair, as in the case of vias.

through simulation and system analysis may never occur in reality, due to routing and protocol effects that may not be captured in a signal integrity simulation.

Intel tools will capture the effects of all-phase and/or in-phase crosstalk, where appropriate to the worst-case behaviors of the interface. Because the aggressors in Intel's three-pair recommended format remain undriven, in-phase and all-phase crosstalk effects are handled mathematically rather than through explicit simulation.

## Jitter

Jitter can result from ISI effects (noted above), as well as noise sources, such as the system power supply and crosstalk from other signals coupled onto interconnect traces. For analysis purposes in time-domain simulation, jitter is typically not included in the driven data pattern or the receiver models. The only jitter modeled as part of the simulation decks provided by Intel is that resulting from ISI and from coupling from other Intel QPI signals. Other sources of jitter are accounted for through the specification and are budgeted in the overall eye template at the receiver pads used for simulation analysis.

## Characterization Locations

For Intel QPI, all of the major performance requirements are defined in terms of eye diagrams. These eye diagrams are defined in two ways:

- minimum eye diagrams for drivers alone
- minimum eye diagrams for a particular combination of components

The first category, for individual components, is defined by the Intel QuickPath Interconnect specification. The specification provides for a simple test fixture to be used at the transmitter, usually a resistive load or transmission line pair of fixed impedance (receivers are characterized using BER).

The eye diagram requirements for many other serial-differential interfaces are defined by industry specifications at specific points in system topologies. For example, the USB specification defines transmitter performance at the transmitter pins and at a connector on the transmitter side of a topology. In both cases, the "receiver" is not a specific active device, but usually a resistive load.

By contrast, for Intel QPI, the model user's guides for particular platforms define the eye diagram at the receiver die pads, with the rest of the system being explicitly modeled. Even the receiver's package effects are included. The receiver itself can be modeled using a resistive-capacitive circuit, as noted above. This makes Intel QPI unique, in that the specific requirements for the bus are defined and may be applied to a simulation that exactly matches the topology of interest.

An example eye diagram for Intel QPI, with evaluation criteria added, is shown in Figure 4.9. This eye mask, when applied to waveforms generated through peak-distortion analysis or from bitstream simulation accounts for the impact of jitter, crosstalk, attenuation and the reflective effects already discussed[6]. Different eye masks are provided for different platform types and speeds (for example, dual-processor servers intended for the efficient performance market segment may use an eye target significantly different from that designed for a mission critical eight-processor system.

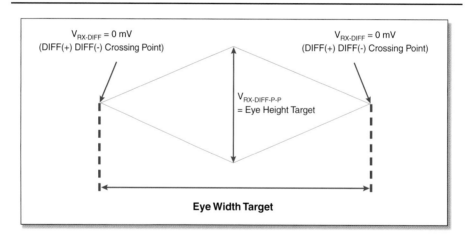

**Figure 4.9**   Eye Diagram with Target Mask

---

6   Note that the example simulation component and system models may not directly include effects such as pair-to-pair mismatch or the impact to Intel QPI signals from signals on other interfaces. These effects are minimized through adherence to the platform design guidelines. In many cases, the eye template provided for the interface has also accounted for these effects, with assumptions derived from the reference design described in the guidelines.

## Electrical Simulation Setup

The overall simulation flow to be used for time-domain simulations using Intel models and tools is shown below.

- A SPICE-based time-domain simulation tool
- Appropriate Intel-supplied models for all Intel component transmitters and receivers (buffers and packages)
- W-element models for all transmission line structures, in 3-pair (6-line) format
- Via, connector, and so on models as either W-elements or equivalent SPICE circuits, also in 3-pair (6-line) format
- One or more simulation decks tying these components together into a full system model
- Appropriate probing points, either at the receiver pad or after its amplifier, in the final simulation deck

Note that any simulations run must cover the variations expected in the system over high volume manufacturing. Variations may include but are not limited to:

- Transmitter and receiver buffer impedances
- Transmitter drive swing
- Transmitter and receiver package impedances
- Transmitter and receiver package routing lengths
- Board trace lengths (per layer, including breakouts)
- Trace electrical parameters (impedance, loss, crosstalk) *or* trace physical and material parameters (width, spacing, pair-to-pair spacing, dielectric constant and loss tangent, dielectric thicknesses)
- Connector physical and electrical variations (impedance, loss, crosstalk)

Users should take into account the overall number of cases and the simulation time taken for any particular case. Methods to cover this range of simulation cases include Monte Carlo variation or any statistical methods appropriate to the real system variations expected. Several sources of additional information on simulation case selection are listed in the References section.

## Simulation Flow

Figure 4.10 shows the general simulation flow recommended for Intel QuickPath interconnects. Intel's SISTAI (Signal Integrity Simulation Tools for Advanced Interfaces) system provides several tools to users to analyze the response of a topology from time-domain simulation and derive an eye diagram, a worst-case set of bits patterns and/or an optimum equalization setting. These online tools all use a pulse response (a single logical one bit sent through a topology from driver to receiver and allowed to settle completely) to characterize the system's response to different types of stimuli. The Bits Patterns tool can calculate worst-case zero and worst-case one signaling levels through superposition by PDA. LTI assumptions mean that the single bit used in the pulse response, along with the settling response of the system, can be mathematically combined through convolution to generate the smallest eye that the system could possibly generate at any bit error rate. The Bits Patterns tool can also provide the corresponding worst-case bit pattern that generates the smallest eye.

A separate tool, Tap Settings, provides the optimum transmit equalization settings for a particular no-equalization pulse response, given the number of taps available in the driver and other information on the system. The tool also provides a calculated eye, also using PDA methods, which would result from the use of the optimum taps. A third tool, Causal W Element, is used before simulation to ensure that time-domain simulation models of traces are truly causal and passive, with the effects of surface roughness and dielectric loss correctly accounted for.

More details on SISTAI are available from Intel's field representatives.

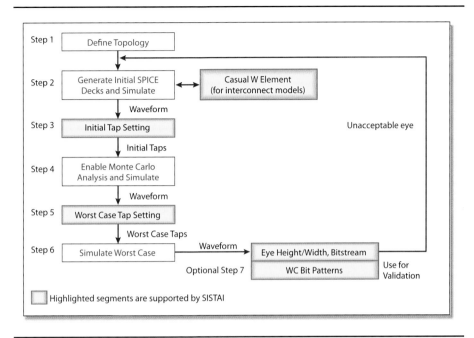

**Figure 4.10** SISTAI Simulation Flow

Users begin with an assessment of the likely worst-case behaviors of the system and ends with the worst-case bit pattern and appropriate equalization settings having been established to ensure good margins at the receiver.

Identification of the expected worst-case topology is not necessarily straightforward. "Worst-case" here means generating the smallest output eye (eye height and/or eye width) at the receiver decision point, usually the receiver buffer pads. For simple server systems, the smallest eye might result simply from very long interconnects on the PCB between the driver and the receiver. Therefore, a worst-case topology would be one with the longest interconnect traces. For a more complex system, involving several connectors and printed circuit boards of varying impedances, shorter routes may result in more reflections and a reduced eye opening due to destructive interference. The relevant engineer's judgment is critical to assessing which links in an Intel QuickPath Interconnect layout are initially most likely to provide worst-case behaviors.

This worst-case topology is then simulated in the time domain, with all equalization turned off. The pulse response of this topology is analyzed using Intel tools under the SISTAI system to establish the appropriate equalization settings to maximize the received eye. If the optimum equalization settings still result in an eye that violates Intel QPI requirements, the system should be redesigned in terms of lengths, stackup and other physical effects to ensure passing performance. If the resulting eye passes requirements, the full design space can be studied.

The next phase involves analysis of the target topology using bit-stream simulations, rather than pulse responses, across process, voltage and temperature variations, plus PCB manufacturing variations, to assess whether high-volume production of the system will result in individual systems that fail the specification. Monte Carlo or other methods of introducing variation into the topology should be used to study the effects of small changes in trace length, stackup parameters, and silicon behavior over the lifetime of production. Individual waveforms are produced, using the worst-case bit pattern from the initial pulse response analysis. If all the resulting waveforms from simulation over the design space still pass, the overall solution space is solid.

If failures are noted, the equalization settings should be recalculated through SISTAI using a no-equalization simulation on the failing topology. The worst-case bit pattern for the failing case with the optimum equalization can then be established using SISTAI again on a pulse response featuring the new equalization setting. Bitstream simulations as before using the new topology can verify the topology's performance versus the specification for small variations on silicon and PCB design parameters.

At the end of the process, a final topology will have been established that satisfies the Intel QPI specifications and features an equalization configuration that compensates for ISI and other loss effects across all expected system variations. In addition, a worst-case bit pattern will be available that can be used both in simulation and in the lab for validation.

## Eye Diagram Analysis

As noted earlier, eye diagram analysis is Intel's recommended method for checking the margins of Intel QuickPath Interconnect topologies in simulation. Eye masks are provided in the model user's guide for particular combinations of components, corresponding to the target BER of the interface and platform. The bitstream eye diagrams and any eye diagrams from pulse response simulations processed through SISTAI should be evaluated against the documented eye masks.

## Frequency-Domain Modeling

As with the time domain, frequency-domain modeling of Intel QuickPath Interconnect involves separating the system into parts and capturing important effects in the models for each part:

■ Drivers

■ Receivers

■ Interconnect

Each of these is described in detail in the following sections.

### Frequency-Domain Transmitter Modeling

Frequency- and time-domain models of transmitters (drivers) are not conceptually different. For most types of serial-differential interface analysis today, both assume LTI behavior. Therefore, a frequency-domain driver model may be limited to a simple R-C representation, so long as the resistance and capacitance are representative of the total load presented by the driver to the system under operating conditions, and are not expected to vary with time, voltage, or buffer state. Note that changes in buffer capacitance and or resistance may result from changes in the buffer's equalization setting. These variations should be taken into account when performing simulations of the buffer.

A frequency-domain model for a buffer can be extracted for a driver model at the transistor-level by simply running an AC sweep and extracting resistance and capacitance values over frequency. These can be used as table-driven data sets for a frequency-domain model of the buffer. Alternately, a set of parallel R-C circuits can be created to represent the buffer's behavior over the bandwidth of interest. Figure 4.11 shows the frequency response for one single-ended side of a USB buffer at a single voltage, and Figure 4.12 shows a simplified behavioral model to approximate it.

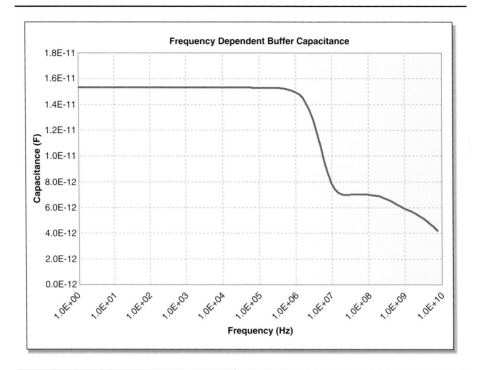

**Figure 4.11** Frequency-Domain Response of a USB Buffer

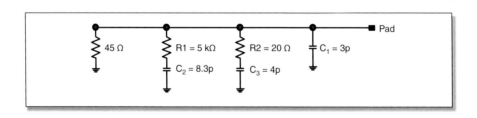

**Figure 4.12** Simplified Frequency-Domain Model for a USB Buffer

Note that I-V tables for a buffer may be used in frequency-domain simulation, even if the I-V tables are nonlinear. However, most simulation engines will linearize the buffer behavior by taking a tangent to the I-V curve at the operating voltage of interest. This will result in a resistive model for the driver being used in simulation for that voltage, even if a resistor is inaccurate to model the behavior of the driver.

### Frequency-Domain Receiver Modeling

Receiver models are, for the frequency domain, no different than transmitter models. As described above, simple R-C representations may be sufficient, either as discrete components or using tables, to capture the behavior of the buffers over the bandwidth of interest.

### Frequency-Domain Interconnect Component Modeling

For the frequency domain, no distinction need be made between interconnect types as was done for vias and transmission lines on the package or PCB, or for connectors, in the time domain above. Each can be represented by a set of network parameters (such as S-parameters) in the frequency domain, so long as the port referencing and attachment points between the components are consistent.

Many field solvers can extract S-parameters from 2- or 3-D models of components such as connectors or even PCB trace layouts. Ports are assigned to the endpoints of the component being modeled and the resulting S-parameters are usually generated assuming a single ideal reference for all ports. So long as each component is modeled using similar assumptions, components may be combined to form a multi-part frequency-domain model of the topology of interest.

Particular care must be taken that each component model is generated so that the S-parameter data is both causal and passive. So long as the data does not exhibit gain, the model may be considered passive. Many software tools and public algorithms exist to check the passivity of S-parameter data. Causality is far more difficult to determine from S-parameter data alone. One method, though clumsy, involves using the model in the time domain with a pulse response. Obvious noncausal behaviors, such as the output of the S-parameter data changing before the input changes, would reveal a problem with the model. Some model extraction tools exist that claim generation or correction of S-parameters to ensure causality. Users should verify these claims before extensive use of these tools. An example of poorly-generated S-parameters causing noise and causality issues in a time-domain pulse-response simulation is shown in Figures 4.13 and 4.14.

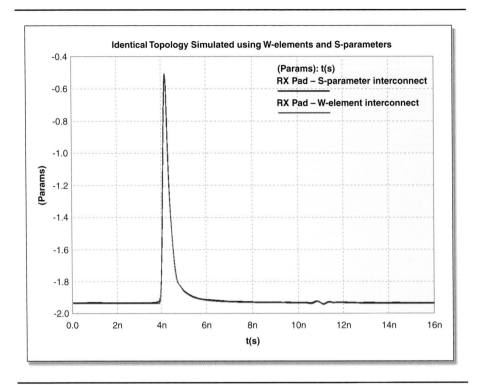

**Figure 4.13** W-element and Poor S-parameter Model Responses for Identical Topologies

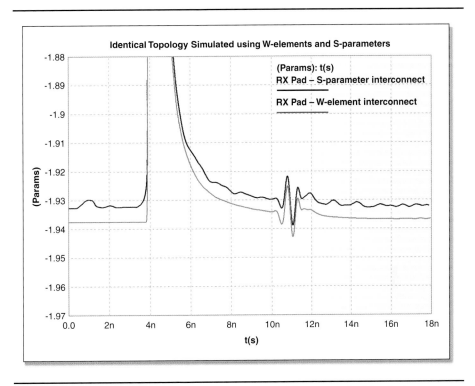

**Figure 4.14** W-element and Poor S-parameter Model Responses for Identical
Topologies, Zoom View

Some simulation engines have difficulty correctly using frequency-domain data such as S-parameters when the step size and bandwidths for the individual portions of the interconnect are not identical. Errors or even engine crashes may result if these dissimilar component models are used together in the same topology.

As a result, users should attempt to ensure that the assumptions and conditions for the extracted frequency-domain models are as consistent as possible. As an extreme example, a 3-D modeling tool containing the physical layout of a topology from one package through a PCB route to another package could be used to extract a single set of S-parameters for the entire signal path, die-to-die. This would ensure consistency among the data for the individual components and would make checking for passivity and causality straightforward. Tools and data capable of supporting this kind of "all-in-one" approach may not be readily available, however.

## Frequency-Domain Analysis

As noted above, analysis in the frequency domain also requires that the driver, receiver, and interconnect portions of the system are causal and passive, as frequency domain simulation assumes steady-state behavior without time-varying (non-LTI) effects. Performing a frequency-domain simulation usually involves extracting S-parameters or similar network parameter data over a given frequency bandwidth.

### Excitation and Bandwidth

Frequency-domain simulation assumes that a source, voltage or current, is used to excite the topology being analyzed at a given frequency or a range of frequencies. In most cases, the source is assumed sinusoidal and the frequencies of interest are continuous in a given bandwidth (most simulation tools provide linear, octal, decade and other intervals for the sweeps in the given bandwidth).

Unlike the time domain, frequency-domain simulation does not involve particular data patterns being used to stimulate the topology directly. Instead, the bandwidth of the frequency sweep must be carefully selected to include the impact of different stimulus patterns plus the maximum edge rate expected from any driver on the topology. The smallest possible upper end for the overall bandwidth will usually be defined by the data rate, while the maximum may result from a harmonic of the data rate (usually the fifth) or the knee frequency from the maximum edge rate of the fastest driver, whichever is highest.

For example, a PCI Express topology assumes 8b/10b signaling, which limits the energy from the fundamental to between the maximum switching rate (101010...) and the minimum switching rate (four ones and six zeros or vice versa, with a single bit as widely separated from other bits of similar polarity as is legal within the 8b/10b protocol). This minimum switching rate defines the smallest upper end for the bandwidth. A larger bandwidth may be set by using the fifth harmonic of the maximum switching frequency as the upper limit (for 5 GT/s, this would be 25 GHz) or the knee frequency derived from the maximum edge rate expected (as noted in Chapter 3). In the case of a PCI Express[†] driver with a 20 ps edge, 20–80 percent, this would result in a knee frequency of 17.5 GHz. The widest bandwidth would therefore use the 25 GHz maximum derived from the fundamental.

## ISI and Crosstalk

The overall approach to including ISI and crosstalk effects in frequency-domain simulations is little different than in time-domain simulations. ISI will be indirectly captured if the simulation deck contains reasonably accurate device and interconnect models. The impact of impedance discontinuities will be seen in the frequency response as apparent losses or gains at particular frequency points. Because frequency-domain simulations are assumed to be steady state, simulation duration is not a concern. Similarly, the three-pair structure recommended for Intel QPI simulations will include crosstalk effects, which also will appear in the frequency domain as apparent losses and/or gains at particular frequency points. No additional work is required beyond the time-domain process to include either ISI or crosstalk in the frequency domain.

## Jitter and Noise

The frequency-domain representation of a system topology makes irregular or time-varying effects difficult to include. Harmonic or sinusoidal jitter may be included in frequency-domain simulation. However, a more straightforward approach is to simply account for jitter and noise impacts as part of an overall loss budget, or to use frequency-domain simulation simply to identify worst-case topologies and include deterministic jitter effects in a time-domain simulation.

## Computing Margins

In general, margins for an Intel QuickPath Interconnect system are difficult to compute directly from a frequency-domain simulation. The results of such a simulation, as noted above, are likely in the form of S-parameters or similar representation not directly comparable to the Intel QuickPath Interconnect specifications.

For best results, frequency-domain simulations may be used to examine and optimize the physical and electrical parameters of a system, or to establish the worst-case combinations based on insertion and return loss. For example, the speed of frequency domain-simulations make them compelling to use for component value and trace routing sweeps to find the maximum loss for a given target topology. These specific combinations could then be analyzed in the time domain, either with the frequency-domain models themselves or their time-domain equivalents, to establish the system's performance versus the eye diagram, as described in Chapter 3 for the time domain.

# Chapter 5

# Printed Circuit Board Design Considerations

Designing a printed circuit board (PCB) layout to include Intel® Quick-Path Interconnect (Intel® QPI) routes requires careful study and great attention to detail. In the process of selecting materials, arranging stackup layers and routing traces, the designer must balance signal performance, routability, inter-signal relationships and other considerations. In this chapter, we present essential advice on designing PCB routes within physical layout constraints while maintaining good signal integrity. Fortunately, for those used to the requirements of PCI Express†, the routing recommendations listed here will be highly similar.

Note that the material in this chapter is general and should not be seen as a substitute for guidance provided in the Intel platform-specific design guidelines. Further, the information here assumes some basic knowledge of PCB layout concepts and good practices. This chapter focuses primarily on the data and forwarded-clock traces of Intel QPI, while compensation pins and strapping options are not discussed in great detail. Contact your local Intel field representative for detailed information on particular platforms.

## Intel® QuickPath Interconnect Channel Topologies

All Intel QPI links, including both the data and the forwarded clock, are configured as point-to-point topologies. The topologies comprise a single transmitter and receiver, both of which are impedance-matched (within the components themselves) to an 85-ohm differential target to minimize reflections. The goal for the PCB designer is to ensure that the interconnect between the transmitter and receiver matches this impedance target as much as possible. This includes minimizing impedance variations between trace routes as well as minimizing discontinuities from features such as connectors or via stubs. This ensures that optimal signal amplitude and duration is delivered to the receiver to achieve the BER requirement.

The different platform types (mobile, desktop, workstation, server, and so on) have different signaling requirements that are dictated by the power and channel performance characteristics. Some platform topologies are simple (for example, a single printed circuit board with no connectors) and others may span up to three printed circuit boards utilizing two connectors between the transmitter and receiver. Whereas some components may only need to operate in a single platform topology, others may need to operate in multiple topologies (for example, the same I/O hub component may be used in a no-connector, single-PCB platform as well as a two-connector, three-PCB topology). The routing of the interconnect signals for each PCB will need to be assessed for the varied channel performance required.

Three different PCB/connector topology combinations are defined for Intel QPI:

- Zero-connector/single-PCB
- One-connector/two-PCB
- Two-connector/three-PCB

Examples of these three topology combinations are illustrated in Figures 5.1 through 5.3.

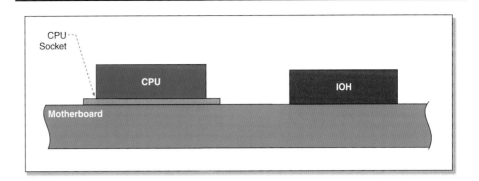

**Figure 5.1**    Zero-Connector/Single-PCB Topology

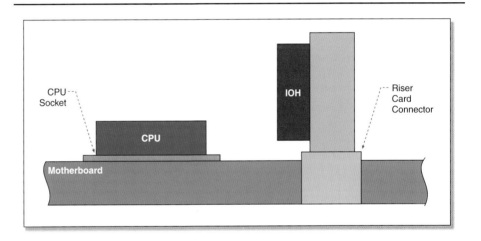

**Figure 5.2**    One-Connector/Two-PCB Topology

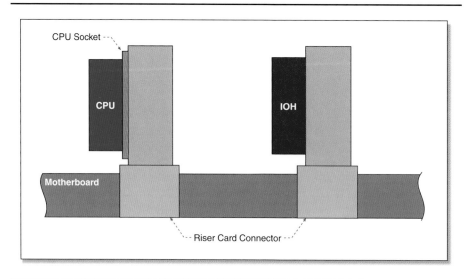

**Figure 5.3**  Two-Connector/Three-PCB Topology

As long as the transmitter-to-receiver path is electrically DC-coupled, other interconnect channel components potentially may be used, but are not explicitly defined. These include such elements as flex PCBs, SMA connectors, and SMB cables. Intel QPI is a ground-referenced architecture, so the proper ground referencing and continuity need to be observed to effectively utilize these types of connection technologies.

The following sections address the design considerations for some of the most common platform components.

## Printed Circuit Board Material Properties

Four central properties of PCB materials determine almost all of the platform's performance: dielectric constant (Er), dielectric loss tangent (TanD), dielectric fiberweave, and copper surface roughness. Dielectric constant shapes the signal propagation velocity and much of the trace impedance. Fiberweave, surface roughness, and loss tangent control the loss of the signal routing. For larger platforms, loss is the most important aspect of the PCB design to control for high-speed designs.

In considering dielectrics, PCB designers should select the type of material best suited for their desired signaling performance targets, also considering cost and manufacturability. Intel QPI designs allow designers to use the common FR-4 dielectric material. However, designers may consider other material options if higher signal performance or longer interconnect channels are needed.

FR-4 PCB laminate material is most commonly used in printed circuit board manufacturing (with "FR" signifying "flame retardant," as defined in the UL94V-0 specification, and "4" indicating woven glass-reinforced epoxy resin). For Intel platform design guidelines, use of FR-4 assumes a nominal dielectric constant of approximately 4.0 and a maximum loss tangent of 0.022 at 1 GHz. These values will vary due to manufacturing and supplied material properties, as well as humidity and temperature conditions.

In general, for Intel QPI platforms, the PCB loss tangent must be kept below 0.022. This target is determined with respect to the worst-case conditions leading to the highest possible loss for a given trace geometry. The American Society of Heating, Refrigerating and Air-Conditioning Engineers (ASHRAE) has published guidance on the environmental conditions appropriate for mission-critical operating computer equipment ("Thermal Guidelines for Data Centers and other Data Processing Environments," 2004). These conditions are primarily oriented to humidity and temperature. While temperature has a generally well-understood impact on platforms—the result of trace resistivity changes from the temperature-sensitive resistance of copper—humidity's effect is less intuitive.

Being composed of a fiber, the dielectric prepreg material separating trace and/or power supply layers can absorb and retain water. This moisture can increase the dielectric loss of the material, because water is itself conductive. The polar nature of the water molecule makes it more easily rotated and therefore makes it more readily able to dissipate energy in the presence of frequency-varying electric fields.

The practical outcome of this limitation is that the 0.022 target value is *the highest that should occur in the board material after assembly of the board, over high-volume manufacturing variations.* While this is easily stated, this may be difficult to achieve, as material datasheets may not cover the worst-case variations over all frequencies or environmental conditions. Further, the physical properties of the material may be changed as the result of the manufacturing process. Finally, the full statistical variation in material properties and manufacturing effects may not be easily obtained.

Because of these difficulties, more recent platform design guidelines are moving to a specification of maximum loss per unit length for PCB traces. This takes all loss sources—dielectric losses, surface roughness effects, and so on—into account and permits design tradeoffs between, for example, trace dimensions and dielectric loss tangent. Because this limits design outcomes and not material inputs, this approach requires more thorough investigation of stackup properties through a field solver plus careful checking of manufacturing capabilities and tolerances. For more information, please consult the design guide for specific platforms.

A variant of FR-4, called halogen- or halide-free (HF), has emerged as a popular dielectric material option. As HF materials contain very low amounts of chlorine or bromine, their decay in landfill space after disposal is thought to pose less risk to human breathing than non-HF materials. HF PCB material Er is generally greater than non-HF FR-4, in the range of 4.0 to 5.0. The loss tangent for HF material is generally equal to or less than FR-4, making the material less lossy. Electrical behavior and performance evaluated with the FR-4 material assumptions need to be revisited if HF materials are considered for PCB manufacturing due to these differences in material properties. As noted in earlier chapters, these changed properties can have a direct impact on PCB characteristic impedance, insertion loss, and crosstalk.

One approach to converting PCB designs from FR-4 to HF materials is to keep all the same stackup geometries and apply them to the new HF PCB material. While this is the easiest option to implement, it is also the option that can have the largest performance degradation in terms of signal integrity. With an HF Er of 5.0, the impedance is reduced by 10.6 percent as compared to a non-HF PCB. Similarly, an HF Er of 4.6 results in an impedance reduction of 6.7 percent. If the impedance targets must remain the same for both HF and non-HF FR-4 PCB designs, the stackup geometries must be adjusted to compensate for these material effects.

To mitigate the lower characteristic impedance of HF materials, the trace widths can be narrowed to increase impedance. This approach can have negative side effects. First, narrower traces increase signal loss, due to increased resistance. Second, a 4-mil trace width is typically the minimum limit for manufacturability and reasonable cost. Finally, adjusting trace widths may not be possible for all board regions, as the breakout trace geometries may be limited by the device ball pitch and size. Adjustments to the main routes without similar adjustments for the breakout may introduce additional impedance discontinuities with negative consequences for signal integrity.

Other, more exotic (and expensive) PCB materials may be used if less signal loss or other electrical behaviors are desired. Intel QPI does not restrict designers to specific types of dielectric material so long as overall signal integrity requirements at the receiver can be ensured.

Measuring loss effectively on a PCB is beyond the scope of this book. However, several references have been provided to help provide guidance in measuring PCB losses. Further, third-party testing services are available worldwide that can help analyze PCB losses through laboratory measurement.

## Stackup Configurations and Tradeoffs

The major considerations in establishing a particular stackup for a platform design are the desired overall thickness of the PCB and the impedance target to be achieved. As mentioned in Chapters 3 and 4, the impedance (both single-ended and differential) of Intel QPI signals must be controlled. Maintaining the interface's nominal 85-ohm impedance will determine the material properties and geometries for the routes on the PCB. Moreover, trying to most efficiently utilize the available routing space or "real estate" across layers may have a performance impact, as described in the sections below.

### Multilayer Signal Trace Routing

In general, stripline routing is greatly preferred for high-speed serial-differential interfaces like Intel QPI. Signals on microstrip routes generate and experience two kinds of crosstalk—forward and reverse—while signals on stripline routes involve only reverse crosstalk in homogenous environments. Stripline is, not coincidentally, also more easily controlled in its impedance variance than microstrip for the same stackup at the same cost. This makes stripline preferable for both impedance control and EMI reasons. The downsides include the possibility of dual-referencing for return paths. In realistic stripline designs, combinations of different material properties around stripline trace pairs may make forward crosstalk something other than zero.

Short lengths of microstrip routes are generally unavoidable. The initial routes away from most components may involve some microstrip routing, if only to "escape" the pins of the component and connect to a via connecting to an inner layer. Designers should avoid having more than one layer transition in any given Intel QPI route.

## Impedance

Many industry-standard interfaces, such as Serial ATA and PCI Express, focus on 100-ohm targets for interconnects, including connectors and PCB traces. The main focus of Intel QPI is server platform designs, which usually feature stackup configurations where a differential impedance of 85 ohms is more desirable.

The key reasons for this are:

- 85 ohms is more easily attained on stripline layers on typical server stackups; as stripline removes forward crosstalk and is less susceptible to EMI effects, it is naturally preferable for high-speed serial-differential interfaces like Intel QPI.

- 85-ohm traces on stripline layers tend to have lower overall losses than 100-ohm traces for the same stackup. As loss is a major limitation to the longer trace lengths needed for Intel QPI, 85-ohm routing is naturally preferable.

Over high-volume manufacturing (HVM), the target impedance will vary per board and even within the same board for similar traces by a given percentage. For Intel QPI, the most cost-effective solution for optimum signal integrity assumes a 17.5 percent variation in differential impedance for microstrip traces and 12 percent for stripline. Note that some manufacturers may be able to attain tighter tolerances without significant increases in cost. Simulations are recommended to establish whether using tighter impedance tolerances could help achieve longer trace lengths or other design tradeoffs.

## Signal Trace Routing

The following sections detail the areas where significant care in interconnect layout is needed, including the trace routes themselves, via placement and usage, escapes and non-trace interconnects.

### Differential Pair Length and Trace Matching

Overall, the total lengths for Intel QPI at 4.8 GT/s can range up to approximately 27 inches. However, the maximum length for an Intel QPI route is not something that can be generally stated for all platforms. Designers must remember that the specific length will be highly dependent on the topology, stackup, trace geometry, and materials selected as well as the HVM variations in the actual manufacturing of the PCB. Intel does provide guidance on effective maximum lengths for specific, assumed stackups. However, simulation is the only method of determining, before layout and fabrication, the effective upper length limit of Intel QPI routing on a custom platform design. Any routing length must meet the electrical specifications for Intel QPI as outlined in Chapter 2.

The maximum achievable trace length may be negatively impacted by a number of design choices, including (a) using unnecessary via transitions, (b) routing through connector pin fields or other structures that may result in coupling effects, and/or (c) adding midbus probe or other logic analyzer structures.

Serial-differential interface design, being based on pairs of traces sensitive to skew, means that each signal trace within a trace pair must ideally be perfectly matched in length to the other line in the pair for minimum skew. Realistic routing involves some mismatches between trace lengths, however. For Intel QPI, traces within a pair must be matched in length to within 5 mils, from the pin of the transmitter to the pin of the receiver, across all layers. This requirement is necessary, but not sufficient, for good Intel QPI signal integrity. Matching within a pair requires tracking of "running skew" within a routing layer. This skew is the difference between the total routed lengths of the signals within the pair measured at any point, relative to the beginning of the trace on that layer (whether the "beginning of the trace" is taken relative to the transmitter or receiver is arbitrary). This is not the same as an average skew. In essence, running skew means a continuous skew or skew that cannot ever exceed 20 mils at any point along the length of the line on that layer.

Additionally, compensation must be carried out within 600 mils, and is best carried out beginning within 125 mils, of the change in routing that produced the mismatch.

Compensation for trace mismatches should be performed as close to the mismatch itself as possible. For example, a mismatch of 100 mils that occurs just outside the pin field of the transmitting device should be compensated with trace route adjustments made very close to the transmitting device (perhaps even within the pin field itself, space permitting). Length mismatches are compensated in many cases by using serpentine routing, as will be discussed in the next section.

The architecture has more flexible rules for matching between different pairs in a system. Within a given link on a port (for example, transmit pairs on port 0), data pairs must be matched in length to the length of the forwarded clock pair. This matching is in terms of UI, as shown in Figure 5.4 for MP platforms (platforms with more than two processors) at 6.4 GT/s, data must be no more than 0.5 UI shorter 3.5 UI longer than the clock. For 4.8 GT/s speeds, the maximum skew for MP platforms shrinks to 2.5 UI (note that the maximum UI value is smaller for slower speeds, but the absolute skew in picoseconds is approximately the same). For DP platforms (platforms with only two processors), the mismatch is generally 0 UI shorter (matched data-to clock pair length) or no more than 2 UI longer, due to the different architecture used in DP systems. As always, individual platform requirements may vary and the specific platform design guidelines should be consulted for details.

At any speed, this skew allowance includes the impact of connectors. Note that routing of the clock in the middle of a group of data pairs can make routing easier. When an entire link's routing must bend, clock-to-data matching rules may be more easily observed if the clock is not on the outside or the inside of the bend, limiting the length of all the data traces.

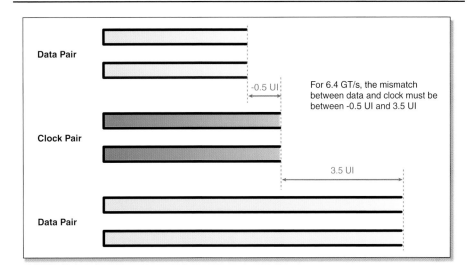

**Figure 5.4**  Data and Clock Pair Mismatch Limits for MP Platforms

With Intel QPI's clock failover capabilities, the failure of the main clock pair may result in an existing data pair being reassigned as a clock. In this situation, the matching rules between the remaining data pairs and the new clock pair must still be maintained.

In general, Intel QPI ports do not have lane-to-lane matching requirements. So, for example, pair 19 on port 0 need not be matched in length to pair 19 or port 1, or any other pair on other ports.

## Bends and Serpentines

Bends in differential pairs introduce, by their nature, a mismatch in the lengths and in the electromagnetic coupling of the traces in the pair. As a result, jitter and other undesirable effects can be introduced when bends are used if sufficient care is not taken in routing.

Sudden changes in direction of a trace can have significant signal integrity impacts. Just as a high-speed automobile or locomotive cannot change directions sharply without either slowing down or making the turn incrementally, so too high-speed signals cannot change direction without causing reflections or other deleterious effects.

Generally, the classic "sharp corner" 90 degrees bend in a trace pair is acceptable but not preferred. Instead, two other options are recommended for making routing direction changes:

■ Chamfered routing

■ Multiple bends at less acute angles

In the case of chamfered routing, the sharpest portion of the bend is removed, as shown in Figure 5.5.

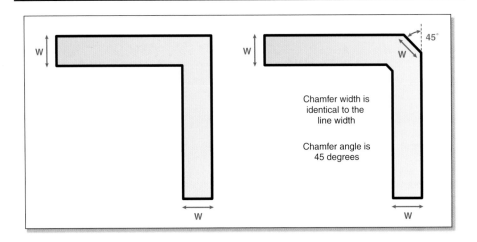

**Figure 5.5** Routing of Trace Bends

The best approach is to route several gradual direction changes using much less acute angles than sharp 90 degrees bends. This can actually reduce overall trace lengths, but may require manual routing as opposed to an automatic function in a PCB design software tool. The simplest gradual approach is to simply create two 45 degrees bends with a separation, in place of a single 90 degrees bend, as illustrated in Figure 5.6.

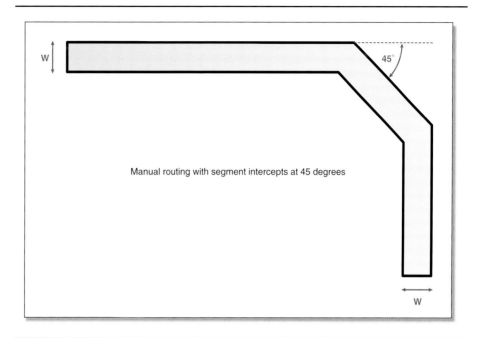

**Figure 5.6**   Routing of Trace Bends for Gradual Direction Change

Serpentines are acceptable and may even be required in order to meet the length matching requirements on traces within an Intel QPI pair, as well as between data and clock pairs. Any serpentine routing must not compromise, however, the minimum spacing requirements of the trace pairs. In other words, any bends must not bring the innermost portions of the pair closer together than the minimum spacing requirement, as shown in Figure 5.7.

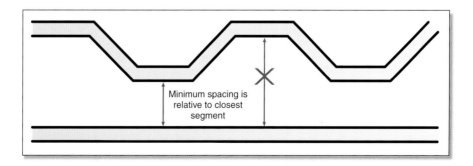

**Figure 5.7**   Minimum Spacing Between Differential Segments

Note that lane pairs may be routed with D+ and D- inverted, using the polarity inversion feature of Intel QPI, discussed below, to assist the platform designer in avoiding difficult routing scenarios.

Overall, serpentine dimensions must be calculated to prevent coupling of a signal to itself. For example, a signal trace may traverse a very short distance in the X direction, from transmitter to receiver, while covering long distances in the Y direction, orthogonal to the direction of signal travel. This means long stretches of parallel trace routes between segments of the same signal. Routed closely enough together, these parallel lengths could cause a signal to be "self-coupled forward" or "self-coupled backward" and so introduce ISI effects.

To avoid this, a minimum spacing must be observed between parallel segments of the same trace routed in a serpentine, as shown in Figure 5.8. This distance is denominated in terms of the height of the dielectric layer used as a reference: for microstrip, this distance is 7 times the dielectric height, while for stripline the distance is only 5 times the dielectric height. This ensures that the trace segments are always more strongly coupled to the reference plane than to each other.

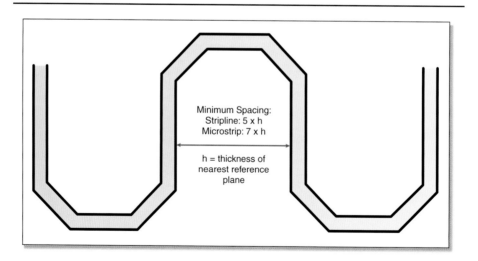

**Figure 5.8**  Recommended Spacing Between Serpentine Bends

Finally, bends in traces can be used to minimize the impact of dielectric fiberweave. For fiberweave mitigation, the critical relationship to keep in mind is between maximum transfer rate and routing length parallel to the weave in the PCB dielectric. The weave material is usually aligned to the edges of the board, which means avoiding weave effects requires routing at an angle relative to the board edges.

To determine the routing length parallel to the weave, determine the root sum square (RSS) of horizontal and vertical lengths aligned to the edges of the board (this assumes the fiberweave is not rotated with respect to the board layout). Ignoring any traces routed at an angle to the edges of the board, this total length is calculated as:

$$Length_{Parallel} = \sqrt{H_1^2 + H_2^2 + ... + V_1^2 + V_2^2 + ...}$$

For 5 GT/s, traces routed parallel to the weave as calculated using the above formula should not exceed 5 inches in length. Lengths for other speeds are listed in Table 5.1.

**Table 5.1** Lengths for Traces Routed Parallel to the Weave

| Data Rate (GT/s) | Maximum RSS Length (inches) |
| :---: | :---: |
| 5 | 5 |
| 6.4 | 4 |
| 8 | 3 |

Practically speaking, minimizing routing lengths parallel to the board edges means regularly introducing a bend in the trace pair at predetermined angles. Industry research suggests that a 45 degrees angle is ideal, but that 10 degrees angles, like those shown in Figure 5.9, are acceptable and practical.

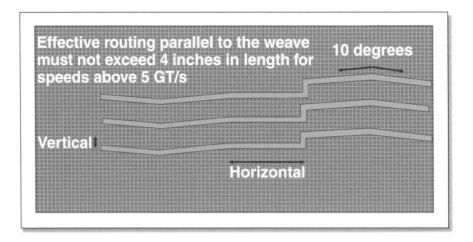

**Figure 5.9**   Recommended Fiberweave Routing Approach

Other methods of fiberweave mitigation include rotation of the entire design (Gerber) plot relative to the dielectric material, or rotating the dielectric material during PCB fabrication. Both methods involve similar trace angles to those noted above. However, both involve significant additional costs and manufacturing complexity relative to angled trace routing.

One important note: as impedance is affected by fiberweave, any impedance coupons on PCBs or PCB manufacturing panels must be subject to the same fiberweave mitigation approach as the PCB design itself.

## Breakouts

Breakouts generally occur near transmitting or receiving components, in order to permit the traces to "escape" the constrained routing region underneath the component packages. The lack of space in this region means narrower traces and closer spacing between adjacent traces and vias. The space constraints also mean a greater risk that differential pairs have significant mismatches in length, effectively making them single-ended in some regions. To ensure good signal integrity, a few key rules must be observed, as shown in Figure 5.10.

- The overall routing length in this region should be minimized, preferably to below 1.2 inches. Serpentines and other practices that might extend the trace lengths in the breakout should be avoided.

- Any serpentines or other routing adjustments to ensure overall matching lengths should be performed within 400 mils of the edge of the component pin field.

- Uncoupled line lengths should be minimized over the entire route length, but within the breakout should be kept under 70 mils.

- Breakout sections usually require narrow trace widths to permit routing around component vias and other traces. Traces must eventually "fan out" or widen to the recommended main routing width to ensure the interface impedance requirements are met. This fan-out must occur within 100 mils of the edge of the pin field.

- Note that escapes from the pads may require direction changes in the routing. To avoid coupling of one portion of a trace to another portion of itself, minimum spacing and angles between trace segments on pad escape routes should be observed, as shown in Figure 5.11.

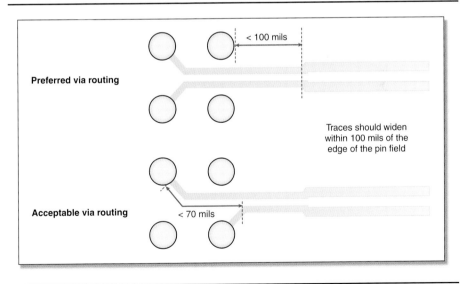

**Figure 5.10** Preferred and Acceptable Routing of Escapes

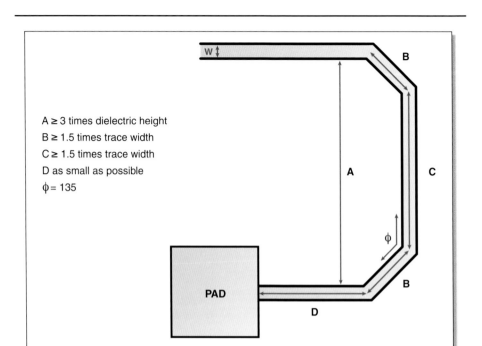

A ≥ 3 times dielectric height
B ≥ 1.5 times trace width
C ≥ 1.5 times trace width
D as small as possible
φ = 135

**Figure 5.11**   Recommended Routing to PCB Pads

## Trace Dimensions and Spacing

The specific dimensions of individual Intel QPI traces and pairs (width, thickness, spacing within the pair and to other signals) will depend on the specific stackup selected for a given platform. The overall platform PCB thickness and desired layer count will help determine the thicknesses of individual layers and, in turn, will help determine the dielectric materials to be used. All of the above, when combined with the target impedances for Intel QPI and other platform interfaces, may result in only a very few options for physical trace dimensions.

Many Intel QPI server platform stackups are similar, making possible some general statements about trace geometries (note that these assume typical FR-4 material; lower-loss materials or materials with significantly different electrical characteristics, such as HF, will alter these guidelines):

- Trace widths should be 5 mils or larger, for both microstrip and stripline routes

- Trace-to-trace spacing within a pair should be 4 mils or larger, for both microstrip and stripline routes

- Spacing to other Intel QPI pairs of the same kind (Tx or Rx) should be at least 3 times the reference dielectric height for stripline and 7 times the dielectric height for microstrip

- Similarly, spacing to other Intel QPI pair types or non-Intel QPI signals should be at least 5 times the reference dielectric height for stripline and 7 times the dielectric height for microstrip

As always, analyzing specific stackup cross-sections using a field solver, in consultation with information from PCB material suppliers and manufacturers, is strongly recommended.

## Non-Trace Interconnect Features

While trace routing is the most obvious aspect of system design that affects platform signal integrity and performance, several other features can have significant impact. These are briefly described in the sections below.

### Vias

The need for vias usually results from either a connector's mounting pins or layer-to-layer transitions. Routing to and from vias follows much the same assumptions as routing in general, including breakout routing. Symmetry should be maintained in order to minimize skews and resultant jitter. Vias should be placed along an axis perpendicular to the direction of trace routing, as shown in Figure 5.12.

Note that non-signal vias, connected to the nearest ground plane, should be placed at regular intervals around and near any group of 4 or more Intel QPI signal vias, preferably within 200 mils (for power vias, a ground via should be placed within 50 mils). This provides a clean return path for signals and noise.

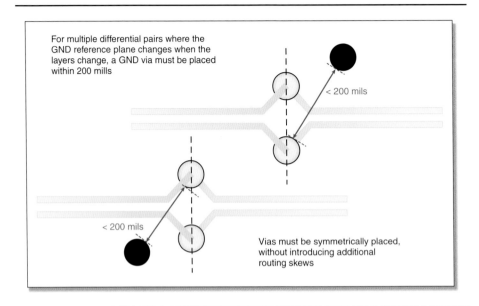

**Figure 5.12** Symmetrical Placement of Vias

Via pads, or large areas of metal connecting to the via on layers where signals are not themselves connected, should be minimized. This keeps additional via capacitance to a minimum. Any via pads on layers where signals are not connected should be removed, as shown in Figure 5.13.

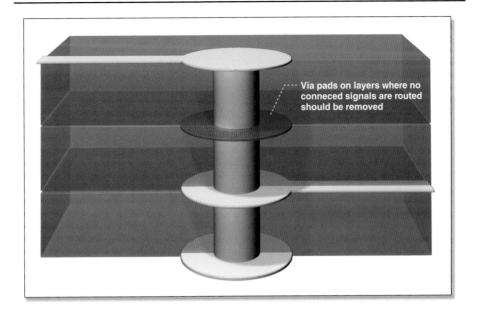

Via pads on layers where no conneced signals are routed should be removed

**Figure 5.13**  Removing Unused Via Pads

As mentioned earlier, the unterminated "stub" portion of vias should be minimized. Careful routing can reduce stub length, including making any internal layer transitions connect between the most separated layers (that is., for an 10-layer board, ensuring that internal transitions occur between layers 3 and 8) In general, Intel QPI routes with via stubs less than 70 mils are acceptable for 4.8 GT/s operation. If the via stub is up to 100 mils long, either inductive compensation or, preferably, back drilling should be performed in order to reduce the effective electrical length of the stub and the consequent reflections. Via stubs above 100 mils in length should be backdrilled, as shown in Figure 5.14.

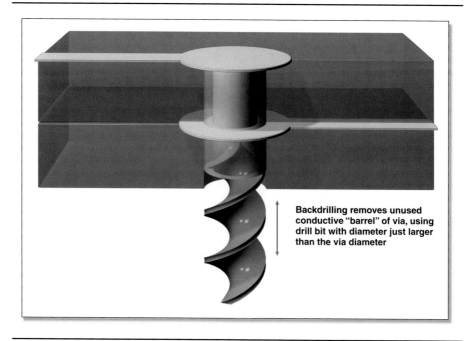

Backdrilling removes unused conductive "barrel" of via, using drill bit with diameter just larger than the via diameter

**Figure 5.14** Backdrilling Removes Unused Via Material

For simple topologies (those without connectors), generally, fewer than four vias should be present on any one route. This will easily accommodate two layer transitions plus a single connector in the routing path. Use of more vias may be possible, but may drive reduced maximum trace length or other tradeoffs. As always, simulation is strongly recommended in such cases.

Test pads may be added to the system, in order to verify the connectivity of the routing. However, these test pads should only be added onto existing vias. The recommended test pad diameter is 26 mils. Note that spacing to other features, such as traces and other vias, may require adjustment in order to accommodate a test pad.

For non-test-pad vias, the via diameter should generally be 10 mils, with a 20 mil pad and a 30 mil antipad.

### Reference Planes

Intel QPI routes should be ground-referenced (in other words, with the traces placed over or with minimal distance to the ground or Vss plane). As noted earlier, this is related to the design of the transmitters and receivers and the resulting need for clean return paths. In addition, a minimum distance between the trace edge and the edge of the reference plane must be maintained; this minimum is 20 times the target width of the trace.

A simple rule for routing Intel QPI traces over splits in reference planes is: *don't*. Generally, routing over plane splits will increase the likelihood of EMI issues plus coupling of noise from other traces. If split-plane routing cannot be avoided, the effects can be minimized by ensuring that the split plane and the traces are separated by a distance at least 3 times the distance between the traces and the ground reference. This ensures that the split plane will not act as a return path for the signal traces.

Routing over antipads (voids in the reference plane to allow vias to pass through the board without shorting) results in short sections of trace without reference planes or with references far enough away that the effective impedance of the trace is dramatically increased. For these reasons, antipad routing should also be avoided. Where possible, the antipads used for differential pairs should be combined into a single antipad.

Finally, via antipads should have a minimum clearance to nearby signals of 20 mils in the case of power or ground signals and 30 mils for signals of the same type (that is, Intel QPI signal routes).

## Connectors

Intel has made available specifications and characterization procedures for connectors to be used with Intel QPI platform designs. Press-fit designs, which feature pins that attach the connector body to the board, are generally acceptable for Intel QPI. For press-fit designs, backdrilling of the pin mounting holes will generally be required. Connector designs that involve no PCB mounting holes for signal pins may be available. However the higher performance of these connectors may come at a significantly higher cost.

Connectors may introduce a hidden PCB routing cost: additional skew. Particularly in the case of right-angle connectors, the individual signals within connector pairs may have a defined amount of electrical skew. Compensation for these skews should be carried out on the PCB traces. However, the overall trace matching rules, described above, should be observed as closely as possible.

Note that routing through a connector pin field may reduce the maximum trace length by as much as 10 inches, due to noise coupling from the connector pins and vias. If no other option is available, routing under the connectors should not use interleaving. Adjacent signal routes under a connector should be of the same direction (Tx-Tx or Rx-Rx). For similar reasons, clocks should be routed under connectors only when absolutely necessary and with the maximum clearance to other signals, preferably not adjacent to other data routes. Note that clock signals should be routed in all cases with large clearances, to prevent noise cross-coupling.

## Probing

In many older bus technologies, direct measurement of signals was possible with minimal effects on system performance. The difference between the signal at the probe point and at the die pad was negligible, and the probe itself represented an insignificant load to the system. The high speeds and edge rates of Intel QPI signals make direct probing much more difficult. The relatively short electrical lengths of the component package routing mean that signals at the die pad will look quite different from signals observed at the component pins or balls attached to the PCB. Reflections can occur within the package that may distort the signal quality at the pin without affecting the quality at the die pad.

Practically, this means that probing for Intel QPI signal integrity validation purposes really cannot be performed at the pins of the receiving device. For similar reasons, probing at test points or in the middle of the bus may also not be particularly useful for signal quality checking. Logical traffic analysis, which is useful for protocol and high-level debug, may however be conducted using one of several specific validation probing methodologies. The platform type and components determine which of methods are available. Below, we describe all of the attach types currently defined. Please refer to the specific Intel platform or component specification for additional information on what is available for a specific platform.

Three attachment methods exist for logic analyzer probing of Intel QPI links: mid-bus probe, interposer, and mirror port. A given platform may support one or more of these to provide visibility into each transmitter and receiver link. Some platforms may make use of multiple types in a single platform (for example interposer and mid-bus probe) to cover all of the links.

The mid-bus probe, as the name implies, allows all of the individual link signals to be probed somewhere along the interconnect channel of the PCB between the transmitter and receiver. A single mid-bus probe footprint has been defined so that logic analyzer vendors can provide a consistent connection mechanism that will attach to the mid-bus footprint pattern. A simplified representation of the mid-bus probe is shown in Figure 5.15.

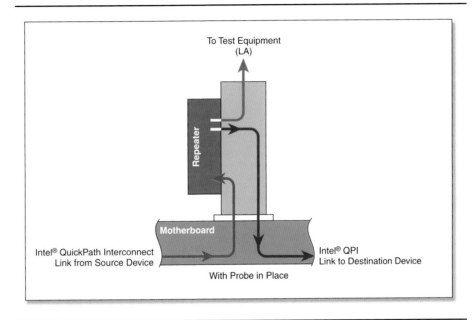

**Figure 5.15** Simplified Mid-Bus Probe

Two types of mid-bus probe have been defined, of which one should be implemented in a single platform. One type acts as an end-agent, and "breaks" the signal path. In this case, the mid-bus probe component receives the transmitted signal from the transmit end of the link and then repeats the signal from the mid-bus probe to the receiver end. This mid-bus probe component is sometimes referred to as a *repeater*. The other type of mid-bus probe does not break the signal path, but instead passively couples to it as the signal passes by from the transmitter to the receiver. This mid-bus probe component is an electro-magnetically coupled probe, or EMCP. The EMCP style of attach mechanisms is illustrated in Figure 5.16.

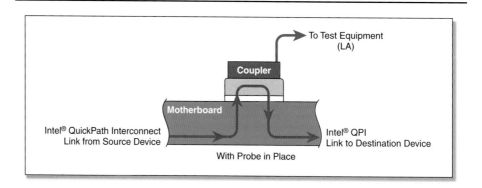

**Figure 5.16** Mid-Bus Probe Using EMCP Coupler

Each of these mid-bus probe types interfere with the transmitted signal, but the design accommodation is different. The repeater, since it breaks the signal path and repeats the signal to the receiving component, must behave like a receiver to the channel transmitter, and like a transmitter to the channel receiver. The benefit to the channel routing is that dedicated transmitters are used and configured specifically for each of the two shorter channels when the probe is in place. However, platform designers must analyze system signal integrity for both the two shorter probed topologies and the longer unprobed topology with a shorting fixture used in place of the repeater probe.

The EMCP probe type also utilizes the same defined footprint as the repeater, but the signals are passed through the mid-bus probe continuing along to the receiver. The EMCP "listens" to each signal through electro-magnetic coupling, adding very slight parasitic inductive and capacitive effects.

Both of these probe attach methods assume the designer has accommodated the probe "footprint" in the routing of the interconnect traces. When the footprint is present, the probe must be populated or a *shorting* structure must be used to ensure signal continuity between the transmitter and the receiver. When implementing the mid-bus footprint in the routed topology, the footprint and the connector will add a capacitive and inductive load, which need to be assessed. In Figure 5.17, the *shorting bar* configuration is shown to illustrate the PCB routed trace impact to the signals.

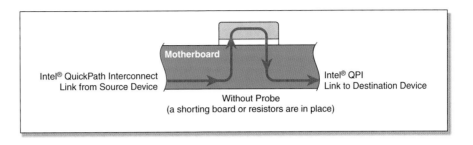

**Figure 5.17** Mid-Bus Probe Shorting Bar

Another logic analyzer probe type is the interposer. This structure is a small PCB that carries a socket for a CPU component and is sandwiched between the CPU and the CPU socket on the PCB. The Intel® QPI signals from the interposer PCB are routed to a local component or "Observability ASIC" on the interposer PCB, which acts exactly like a mid-bus probe repeater or EMCP. The ASIC sends copies of the Intel® QPI signals for analysis to the logic analyzer unit via ribbon or flex cables, while also preserving as much as possible the original signal path to the system receiver. This approach allows checking of a limited number of signals being transmitted by the CPU, with minimal additional signal integrity impact on the transmitted signals. A typical interposer configuration is shown in Figure 5.18. Similar to the mid-bus probe, the discontinuity and channel loading characteristics, while small, need to be assessed to make sure that the channel signal routing will accommodate the load of the interposer. Unlike the mid-bus probe, the in-socket interposer does not require significant PCB alteration to accommodate it and may only call for some additional height clearance around the CPU.

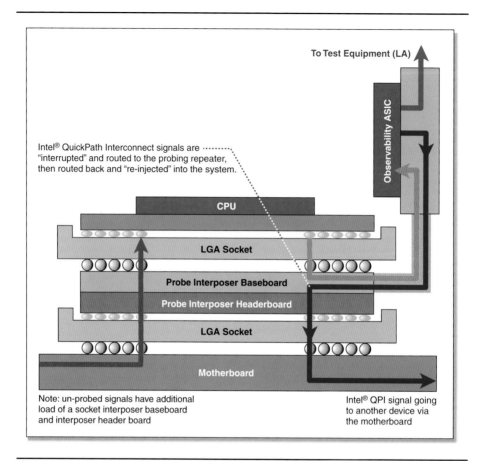

**Figure 5.18** CPU In-Socket Interposer

The third type of logic analyzer connection method is the mirror port. This attach mechanism does not directly interfere with the Intel QPI signal routing on the PCB, as it "taps" copies of the signal generated by separate drivers at the Processor package itself. The mirror port configuration is shown in Figure 5.19.

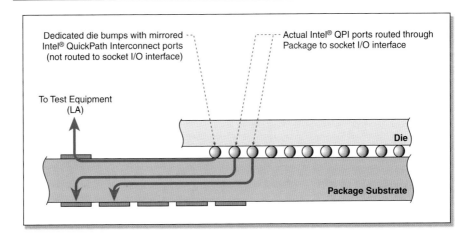

**Figure 5.19** Mirror Port Probe Configuration

## Routing and Intel® QuickPath Architecture

One of the advantages of Intel® QPI is that the architecture itself provides more flexibility to the layout engineer than many other interface types. Specifically, some devices support features such as polarity inversion and lane reversal, which help to ease the burdens of component placement and signal routing by allowing re-configuration of the interface connectivity. The specifics of both these methods are described below.

### Polarity Inversion

PCB designers may face conflicts when trying to optimize component placement while following the interconnect length and routing requirements. The orientation of the components and connectors involves a specific interconnect trace numbering, which may be difficult to maintain in the face of routing density and layer transition requirements. For example, to maintain the correct connections between specific transmitters and receivers, some signals may need to be crossed with respect to one another, as one would tie shoelaces or a bowtie. Such crossing may make following length matching requirements difficult.

To address these issues, Intel QPI supports *polarity inversion*. When polarity inversion is active, the positive and negative terminals in a particular link are reversed, per lane, at the receiver. All Intel QPI components must be able to detect whether each QPI lane has an inverted differential signal. Once detected, the receiver can correct the connections for any of the lanes, on a lane by lane basis.

This capability allows the printed circuit board designer to choose how any of the Intel QPI transmitters, or even the forwarded clock, are connected to the receivers across any lanes. This way, any interconnect trace crossings can be avoided on the printed circuit board, potentially reducing or eliminating the need to match trace lengths of the traces within the pairs. Figure 5.20 illustrates polarity inversion on a simple interconnect (indicated by three tildes in the lane), where the receiver has inverted signal polarities to compensate for the routing used. Note that polarity inversion can be particularly useful when matching lengths between transmitter and receiver breakout regions, as illustrated in Figure 5.10.

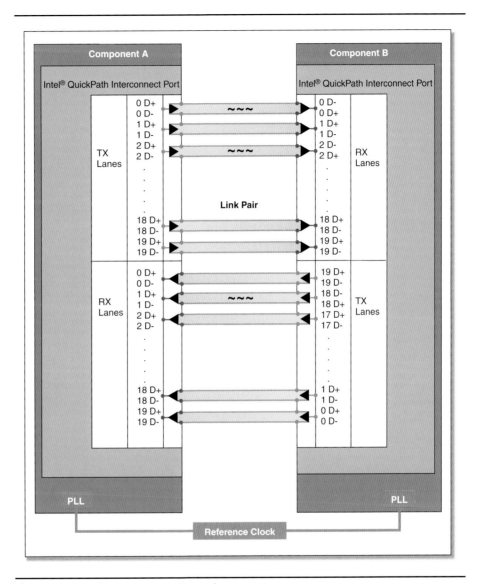

**Figure 5.20** Polarity Inversion Example

## Lane Reversal

As with the signals within a trace pair, lanes also have a specific, assumed arrangement or order with respect to the transmitting and receiving components. As a result, for more complex layouts, entire lanes may cross over one another between interconnected components in a printed circuit board. This can complicate routing, including both the ability to make the connection as well as observance of length matching rules. In extreme cases, maintaining the order of the lanes could require more layers or layer changes to accommodate the trace routing. To ease routing problems due to lane ordering, Intel QPI supports *lane reversal* within each transmit or receive link.

Lane reversal permits reversal of all of the lanes within a link (selective reversal of specific lanes is not supported). For a full-width link of 20 lanes, all 20 receiver pin number assignments are re-mapped to the reverse order of the transmit pin number assignments. So RX0+ remaps to RX19+, RX0- remaps to RX19-, RX1+ remaps to RX18+, and likewise for all other receiver pins. This remapping of receiver pins is illustrated in Figure 5.21, in the link from Component B to Component A.

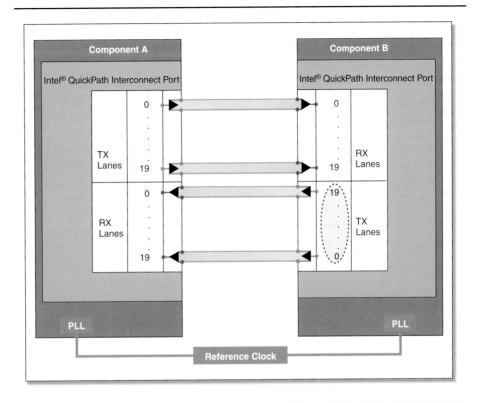

**Figure 5.21** Lane Reversal Example

# Chapter 6

# Measurement and Validation

To ensure that the Intel® QuickPath Interconnect (Intel® QPI) specifications are met, the design electrical performance for transmitters, receivers, and interconnect must be validated. The equipment and measurement methods need to use the same definitions used for the component and PCB design and simulation, so that the simulated predictions can be compared to the measurements. Setting up the test equipment and acquiring the data correctly are critical to this validation. After reading this chapter, you will understand the equipment requirements and measurement methods to validate the electrical specifications and board design.

## What Is Intel® QuickPath Interconnect Validation?

Once the Intel QPI design is completed and fabricated, it needs to meet the specification functional and electrical requirements. Most of the electrical validation is performed with use of a tester or other equipment with a measurement setup and methodology that has a well-defined load (for transmitter specifications) or an input condition (for receiver specifications). Some of the measurements are performed at the platform level to include the board design performance impact.

The intent and focus of this chapter is to provide the key validation concepts, equipment, and methods to apply to Intel QPI designs. The specific details required for individual implementations will need to be obtained from either the component or electrical specifications themselves. This chapter information serves as a companion to the specifications and is not intended to replace them for actual designs.

Most of the electrical specifications are defined to effectively measure and characterize the individual transmitter and receiver independent of the platform type used. This allows the intrinsic component electrical performance to be validated without platform dependence. Most of the validation measurements are geared towards the component silicon developer validation with a tester or bench design validation setup.

There are also some platform-level measurements that either provide the basis for correlation to simulation such as trace, via, or connector elements or that verify the board design for high volume manufacturing health. So, once the component electrical behavior is validated and the PCB interconnect channel elements are extracted, the performance can be compared between measurement and simulation. These types of measurements can be made with an oscilloscope for time-domain reflectometry (TDR) or time-domain transmission (TDT) or a vector network analyzer for S-parameters. In addition to these element measurements, direct end-of-channel measurements can be made at a receiver reference point utilizing the Intel QPI Load Board (QLB) to check the platform-level or system electrical performance quality.

Validation tests of the platform design itself also provide an important measure of Intel QPI interconnect channel quality. Because of the link high operating speeds, complexity of de-embedding the scope measurements, and large number of platforms that would need to be tested to ensure high volume manufacturing quality, Intel provides the capability to use non-intrusive, on-die margining tools via Intel® Interconnect Built-in Self Test (Intel® IBIST). With the results of IBIST combined with statistical methods, the validator is able to obtain measurement of Intel QPI health over a wide range of manufacturing variation.

Upon power-on each Intel QPI link, to become operational, exits the reset state and then proceeds through the initialization and training steps as outlined in Chapter 1. This is the standard operational behavior followed by a link to arrive at the L0 state, which is the active link state for transmitting and receiving data packets. For test and validation measurements, the link comes up into a different state, which can be forced by termination (compliance), or trained or forced/tuned (loopback). Some of the specifications (transmitter, clock) only need a fixed pattern to be transmitted, but some (receiver) need to have receiver-side operation to loopback and compare data patterns.

To perform the electrical measurements, validation and correlation, the measurement equipment needs to be defined. The type of measurement equipment to use depends upon the specification. In some cases multiple types of equipment may be used for a single specification, and in others only a single type of equipment is required.

## Measurement Equipment

The Intel QPI electrical specifications to be measured and validated include AC voltage (including jitter, various voltage cases, and rise/fall times) DC voltage, and resistance specifications. The key types of measurement equipment needed for validation of most specifications are the oscilloscope and the bit-error rate tester (BERT).

Some of these measurement devices can be further divided into sub-categories (such as real-time and equivalent-time oscilloscopes). Also, there are minimum capability requirements for the measurement equipment, so one needs to select a vendor and equipment model that satisfies the requirements.

For recent technologies including PCI-X and Intel Front Side Bus (FSB), equivalent-time (also known as *sampling*) oscilloscopes were used. With a high bandwidth and display set to infinite persistence, the signal data would be collected visually with markers or other means. Some of the Intel QPI measurements can still use the equivalent-time sampling scope, but the way that Intel QPI specifies jitter and timing requires use of real-time sampling scopes for some measurements.

In addition to the oscilloscope and BERT, some other useful measurement equipment is available for specification (DC) validation including the parametric measurement unit (PMU), the digital multimeter, and in-system frequency-domain measurement with a vector network analyzer (VNA).

These are not required for most of the validation, and will not be covered in detail here.

## Oscilloscopes

Oscilloscopes sample and save an analog signal or waveform in one of two basic ways: real-time sampling or equivalent-time sampling. The real-time sampling oscilloscope measures multiple points within a single waveform as shown in Figure 6.1. The measurement samples are made at time intervals, based on the sampling rate. This is an ideal type of scope to capture individual triggered events, unique signal cases, and is best suited for jitter measurements. The equivalent-time scope (also sometimes called a sampling scope even though both types technically "sample" the signal waveforms) samples the signal waveform once per trigger. This type of scope is better suited for measurement of repetitive signals or events.

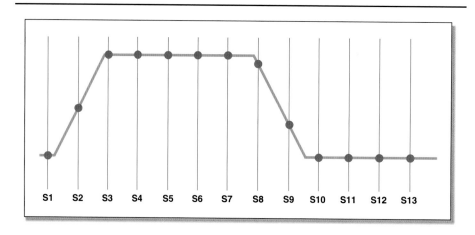

**Figure 6.1**   Real-time Oscilloscope Sampling

Unlike a real-time sampling oscilloscope, an equivalent-time sampling scope samples the waveform once per trigger. The scope is triggered multiple times. By then varying the delay between the trigger and sample, a composite picture of the waveform is built up and transmitted to the scope's display. The delay between the scope trigger and waveform sample can be varied randomly or by introducing a very small delta between consecutive trigger/

sample pairs. The display is built up using a composite of all the samples, as shown in Figure 6.2.

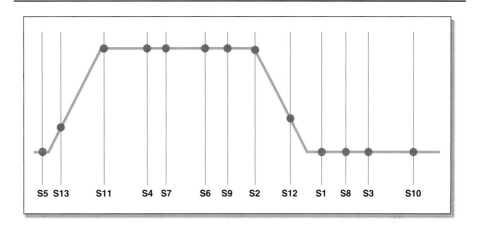

**Figure 6.2**    Equivalent-time Oscilloscope Sampling

The real-time oscilloscope is best for capturing an individual waveform or a sequence of waveforms, since it collects multiple sequential points in the signal stream as shown in Figure 6.1, which are stored digitally and can be analyzed or post-processed. It can also capture UI-to-UI or across-many-UI time and voltage variations. For this reason the real-time oscilloscope is useful for jitter measurements.

This sampling method comes with a cost, which is the bandwidth. Since it measures each signal stream using the same sampling interval, the interval must be sufficiently small to capture the frequency content of the signal. To avoid undersampling, or aliasing, the sampling rate must at least satisfy the Nyquist criterion, which here means that the rising or falling edge must be sampled at least twice.

The requirement for Intel QPI measurements up to 6.4 GT/s is for the oscilloscope to have a bandwidth of at least 13 GHz, and sampling at a rate of at least 40 Giga-samples per second on all four channels. The jitter floor needs to be less than 1 picosecond for N-UI Jitter, for N ≤ 12. The oscilloscope probes and cables also need to have a minimum bandwidth of 13 GHz.

The equivalent-time sampling oscilloscope with bandwidth ≥ 50 GHz and RMS trigger jitter < 200 femtoseconds may also be used for validation of some of the specifications, such as rise and fall edge rate and UI average.

This type of scope typically has a higher analog bandwidth and lower noise floor that is more suited to sample fast rise time signals than a real time scope. But the sampling scope is not suitable to capture UI-to-UI jitter or N-UI jitter, something a real time scope is capable of capturing.

## Effects of Probe Capacitance

Another source of signal measurement interference is the effect of the probe on the signal being measured. At gigahertz frequencies and higher, the probe input capacitance can significantly alter the signal behavior. For example, an oscilloscope probe with a 1.0 pF input capacitance placed at the termination point with a 4.8 GT/s data transfer rate will have an effective impedance of about 33 ohms as shown in Equation 6.1.

---

**Equation 6.1**  Scope Probe Impedance

$$X_c = \frac{1}{2 \times \pi \times 4.8\,\text{GHz} \times 1.0\,\text{pF}} = 33\,\Omega$$

---

Intel QPI data and forwarded clock termination nominal differential impedance is 85 ohms ($\Omega$). With this probe placed in parallel, the effective termination impedance becomes 24 ohms, which is less than one third of the Intel QPI termination. This will affect the data or clock signal return loss due to the impedance mismatch.

For the measured circuit, both the package and scope input impedance include complex magnitude and phase quantities that interact. For modeling and simulation correlation to measurement, the effects need to be included in simulations to assess the circuit behavior as observed compared to without scope interference from capacitance and impedance.

## Other Scope Inaccuracies

In addition to scope bandwidth and probe capacitance, there are other scope inaccuracies to take into account to effectively filter out the signal measurement effects from the intrinsic signal measured. The other significant measurement accuracy detractors are the oscilloscope rise time, noise floor, and gain effects.

If the signal rise time (or fall time) is in the range of the oscilloscope rise time, then the measured signal rise time will be affected (slowed) by the oscilloscope rise time. The ratio of the signal rise time to the scope rise time results in a measurement error as shown in Figure 6.3. For example, if the signal to scope rise time ratio is 3/2, then the scope will measure a 20 percent increase in signal rise time. At just twice that signal to scope rise time ratio, 3/1, the increase is down to 5 percent.

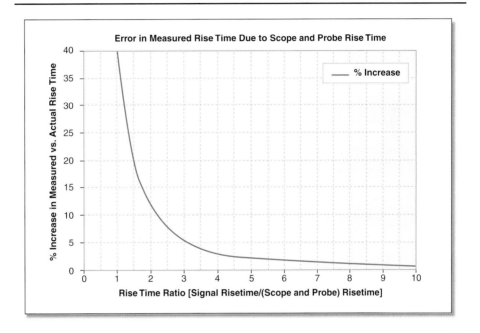

**Figure 6.3**   Measured Error Due to Scope/Probe Rise Time

The oscilloscope noise floor is the base noise from the scope equipment measurement circuits. This noise is present with or without the external circuit there, and limits the measurement resolution. The noise is comprised primarily of random thermal noise from the semiconductor elements, and is typically proportional to the scope bandwidth. The noise has a statistical profile, as shown in Figure 6.4, which is treated as a Gaussian distribution.

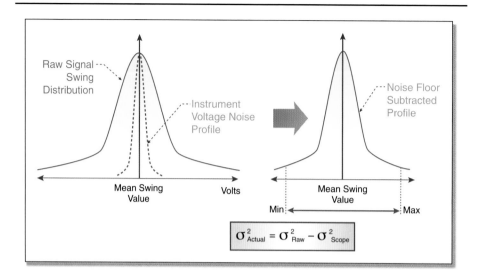

**Figure 6.4**   Instrument Voltage Noise Floor

The oscilloscope noise floor is from the scope alone, independent of any external circuit element noise. The actual circuit noise is calculated by subtracting the scope noise from the measured signal because the scope noise floor is independent of the measured circuit noise (no dependent terms). This is calculated as shown in Equation 6.2.

**Equation 6.2**   Derivation of Actual Signal by Subtracting Noise Floor

$$\sigma^2{}_{Actual} = \sigma^2{}_{Raw} - \sigma^2{}_{Scope}$$

Since oscilloscope measurement circuits are designed to perform accurate measurements, the noise floor may be different for the multiple display scale settings. As shown in the Figure 6.5, measurements of scope noise at 20 mV, 50 mV and 100 mV yield different noise floor values, with the noise floor increasing as the display scale increases. So the noise floor values need to be measured and applied for the scales utilized.

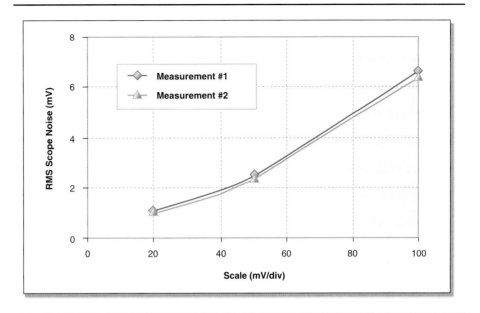

**Figure 6.5**    Noise Floor Measurements at Different Oscilloscope Display Scales

In addition to measuring the scope noise floor at the different display scale settings, the measurement circuit may need to be different to apply to different specifications. For example, the noise floor circuit for transmitter AC common mode voltage uses a different voltage source at the scope input (200 mV) than the voltage source used for the receiver AC common mode voltage (500 mV), as shown in Figure 6.6, where the box with an "X" is the voltage source for both differential input signals.

Other major sources of measurement inaccuracy include DC gain, offset errors, and errors due to the sampling scope's digital to analog (D/A) conversion. DC gain errors (GA) represent the inaccuracies in the scope's Volts/Division gain setting, and are usually specified as a percentage of the deflection from the vertical centerline of the scope display.

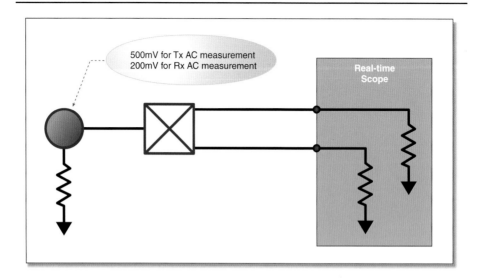

**Figure 6.6**    Voltage Source Setup for AC Common Mode Scope Noise Floor

Offset errors (OA) are introduced when the user adds an offset to the input signal or uses the scope's "position" knob to adjust a signal so that it can be displayed on the scope screen. Finally, integral nonlinearity (INL) errors represent deviations from the straight line DC transfer function. These errors represent the effective resolution of the sampling scope's D/A converter. Adding all these errors together we arrive at Equation 6.3, which represents the measurement bounds for a typical scope's measurement error.

**Equation 6-3**    Measurement Accuracy Bounds Due to Scope Measurement Accuracy

$$measurement\_bound = measurement \pm (GA + OA + INL + NFpeak)$$

The individual values to use for gain error, offset error, integral nonlinear error, and noise floor are dependent on the oscilloscope make and model. However, it is possible to make a couple of general observations:

- When measuring the vertical opening of an eye diagram, use the smallest volts/division setting practical such that the waveform fills the vertical dimension of the display without clipping. In this way, errors due to noise floor and INL are minimized.

- Do not apply position offset or adjustment offset to the waveform. In this way, OA errors are eliminated. Given that Intel QPI transmitter and receiver signals are DC coupled, this should not be a problem for measurements.

It is recommended that the oscilloscope jitter floor is verified, which can be performed by:

1. Generating a 6.4 Gigabit per second clock signal from a pattern generator (such as Agilent† JBERT or SyntheSys† BERTScope) with no jitter injection (this means ≤ 100 femtoseconds RMS edge jitter);

2. Capturing minimum 1 million UI samples with the scope; and

3. Computing RJ jitter floor from scope measured waveform using jitter calculation post-processing.

The N-UI jitter floor should be less than one picosecond for up to $n$UI (where $n$ is determined by platform type. For example for large-scale MP $n = 12$, or for a dual processor socket platform type $n = 9$).

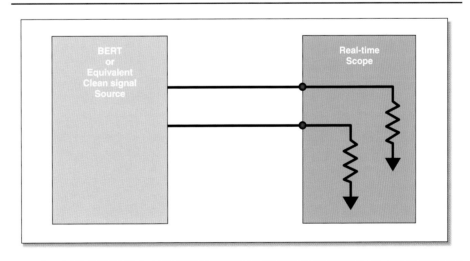

**Figure 6.7** Jitter Floor Measurement Setup with BERT

Transition time converter and/or transmission line trace (with similar routing length as from device under test (DUT) to SMP connector or equivalent) may be used to mimic realistic rise time seen by the scope. All single cases of data collection by a real time scope are assumed to be one shot (triggered by the first data edge and all consecutive data collected without further triggering). If the available memory is not sufficient to complete these tests, repeated measurements should be made and the results combined.

## Bit Error Rate Testers

The bit error rate tester (BERT) measures and records the data bit errors received from the component under test. The BERT should have a capability of at least 10 GT/s signaling due to likely future requirements. This capability includes clock data recovery (CDR), jitter and noise injection functions (JBERT). The basic BERT setup is illustrated in Figure 6.8.

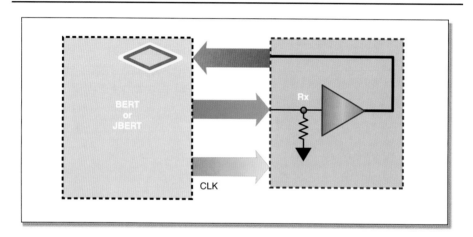

**Figure 6.8**   Basic BERT Setup

## Measuring and Validating the Specifications

The Intel QPI specifications are defined in such a way that they can be validated directly (transmitter, clock) or indirectly (receiver), but in either case by use of a calibrated test setup. This is different than platform or in-system validation, in which the validation assumes the component and channel-intrinsic properties of a given platform set of components.

Most of the transmitter and receiver specifications are validated with the transmitter configured in either a compliance or loopback test mode. These states can be used in either test or in-system configurations. The Intel QPI compliance and loopback state machines are illustrated in Figure 6.9. The compliance mode is typically entered if a test load is detected on the transmitter lanes. It can also be a forced test mode. The loopback mode is used for the receiver margining tests and some transmitter pattern-based tests to elicit worst-case system-like behavior.

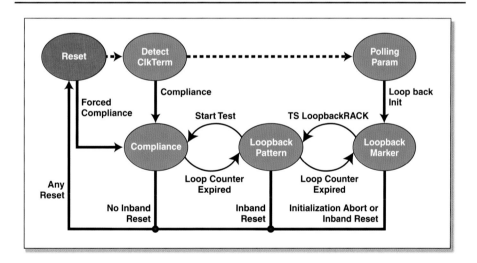

**Figure 6.9**    Compliance and Loopback

Even though most of the validation measurements are performed in a test setup, there are useful in-system measurements to be made. A measurement of the signal eye at the receiver pin location (for example in a socket or SMP connector on a load board) is valid in that it does reveal what the receiver "sees." Assuming that a receiver package reference point meets the channel design guidelines, the measured eye will be representative of the receiver pin eye under similar channel characteristics. Also, the data to clock lane skew at the receiver needs to be measured in-system. In addition, transmitter eye measurements can reveal functional defects, such as the lack of de-emphasis, or gross waveform problems.

## Validation Measurements

The validation measurement methods and configurations depend upon the type of specification being validated. The reference clock, transmitter and forwarded clock, and receiver have specific test loads and measurement points defined to provide consistent measurement values and to compare to simulated performance. All of these specifications are directly measureable except for one type of specification: receiver margining specifications.

The receiver margining specifications are validated by indirect voltage and timing margining tests that measure the resultant BER. These specifications are component-level specifications and are not measured in a board-level design. For the board design, margining tests to verify the Intel QPI interconnect health are performed with Intel IBIST tools, which are available to Intel customers.

## Common (Platform-Independent) Specifications

The common specifications include the multi-UI parameters, reference clock, termination, and some clock phase specifications. These apply with the same specification values independent of the implementation or platform type.

### Multi-UI based Parameters

The multi-UI parameters all are specified in terms of unit interval (UI). Most of these parameters are defined to limit or control the logical design behavior, so are in terms of multiple UIs (not fractions of a UI). The bit error rate (BER) is one of these parameters, and is dependent upon the UI, since each UI is a data "event". The BER is a measure of errors per number of transmitted events.

The UI-based parameters are dependent on the UI definition, but since they are parameterized in units of UI, they are the same values regardless of the data transmission frequency. The UI measurement, $UI_{avg}$, however is an exception and needs to be performed for each operational frequency, and is defined as the average size of the extracted UI over $N_{MIN-UI-Validation}$. All specifications that reference the minimum number of UI to measure being $N_{MIN-UI-Validation}$, are measured for 1,000,000 UI.

There are some multi-UI and sub-UI parameters that are platform-dependent. These parameters include transmitter and receiver jitter specifications (sub-UI), and data to forwarded clock skew (multi-UI). The platform-dependent nature of these parameters was discussed in Chapter 2, and they will be covered later in this chapter.

### Bit Error Rate

Bit error rate (BER) is a measure of how reliably a system can transmit data without failure. Specifically, BER is a measure of the probability that a data bit will be successfully transferred between a transmitter and receiver. For example, if a system has a BER of $1 \times 10^{-14}$, there is a 1 in $10^{14}$ chance that any single data bit will be interpreted incorrectly at the receiver. Another way of stating this measurement is that, on average, one out of every $10^{14}$ bits transferred is received incorrectly.

BER is tied directly to the amount of random jitter (Rj) present in the system. Random jitter is assumed to have a Gaussian distribution with an unbounded maximum value. If a specific jitter profile is known, it should be used instead of a Gaussian distribution. While a system might be designed to be very tolerant to jitter, it cannot be completely free of errors due to the unbounded nature of the jitter. The system design must allocate the total jitter budget of the transmitter, receiver, and interconnect so that the system not only meets the voltage and timing specifications, but that the random jitter does not cause the system to exceed a maximum BER of $1 \times 10^{-14}$.

For Intel QPI components in any platform or configuration, the BER specification is that each lane must have no more than 1 error per every $10^{14}$ bits transmitted. This is the raw in-system BER, before any CRC detections, so that the BER pertains to the transmitter to receiver interconnect and physical layer performance margins.

A number of specifications are validated to a BER other than $1 \times 10^{-14}$. These specifications are jitter and receiver margin specifications that are defined to utilize lower BER values, to allow for realistic testing times and are mathematically evaluated to extrapolate to the needed level of performance. These specifications are covered in the platform-dependent section.

*Tx and Rx Termination Parameters*

The transmitter (Tx) and receiver (Rx) terminations have three defined states. Each termination state has an impedance range defined. The link detect and high termination impedances are common specifications, but the low termination impedance is platform-dependent. The termination ranges are shown in Figure 6.10, which illustrates the clear separation between these three termination impedances. Impedance range margin is built into these termination values to ensure unambiguous state sensing and operation. Three termination states are defined for the Tx (low, link detect, high) and two for the Rx (low, high). The transmitter is solely responsible for detecting the receiver termination—the receiver never detects transmitter-side termination.

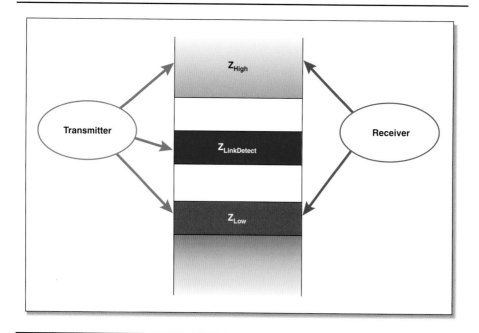

**Figure 6.10** Tx and Rx Termination Ranges

To detect the receiver termination strength, the transmitter has a link detect circuit, which resides on the transmitting component. The link detect circuit will typically be a voltage divider circuit, as shown in Figure 6.11. The link detect resistor pull-up voltage is component-specific with a minimum design tolerance for link compatibility. Given that the voltage divider needs to distinguish between a low impedance (for example between 38 and 47 ohms) and a high impedance (≥ 10 K ohms), the link detect impedance range of 500 to 2000 ohms ensures the two impedances will be correctly detected.

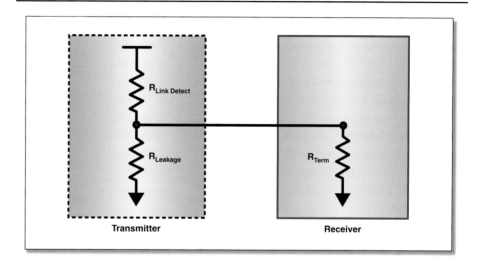

**Figure 6.11** Link Detect Circuit Example

To validate the termination states, all of the measurements are DC voltage measurements. These measurements can be performed with a digital multimeter or suitable parametric measurement unit.

For each of the transmitter termination cases, the transmitter is turned off, so that only the termination is measured. For the high impedance state, all but the last termination leg is disabled. For the link detect measurement, the link termination resistor is on. For the low impedance state measurement, the voltage is swept across the single-ended voltage swing range (independently for D+ and D- signals of the pair), and the V/I point is chosen at Vswing/2.

For each of the receiver termination cases, there is no driver circuit to turn off. Similar to the transmitter, for the high impedance state, all but the last termination leg is disabled and the DC resistance is measured. For the receiver low termination, the voltage is swept to capture the V/I point at Vswing/2 for the D+ and D- signals using the method for the transmitter low termination measurement.

*Transmitter Equalization Testing*

Intel QPI equalization needs to be provided at the transmitter for all transmitters in each system. The exact number of taps and magnitude of tap coefficients to be loaded during link initialization depends upon the individual platform and topology, since the purpose of equalization is to present an optimal signal at the receiver at the end of the interconnect channel. Considering that an individual transmitter may be programmed to one of many different equalization settings depending upon the interconnect channel characteristics, exhaustive setting validation would be extremely time consuming. So, the validation approach is to check the DC de-emphasis measured versus theoretically calculated.

The transmitter equalization is measured at the transmitter output pin, as are the other transmitter specifications. DC measurement of equalization is specified accounting for resistive drops along package and short PCB traces. A calculated amount of dB of de-emphasis is to be set and then the resultant differential voltage for a steady "1" pattern is to be measured. The fully emphasized voltage (V0) compared to the de-emphasized voltage (V0_de) is illustrated in Figure 6.12.

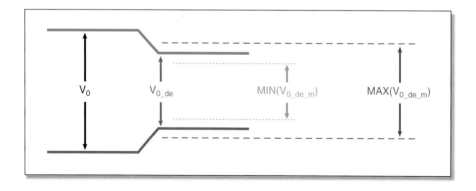

**Figure 6.12** Transmitter Equalization Error

The differential voltage needs to be within a certain error margin, compared to theoretical calculations. In Figure 6.12, V0 is the differential voltage with no de-emphasis and V0$_{de}$ is the theoretical value of the de-emphasized voltage, given by Equation 6.4:

---

**Equation 6.4** Theoretical De-emphasized Voltage Value

$$V0\_de = V0 \times 10^{(-x/20)}$$

---

In Equation 6.4, $x$ is the de-emphasis in dB ($x \geq 0$). In most cases V0 (the differential voltage without any de-emphasis) turns out to be equal to the transmitter differential output voltage parameter ($V_{Tx\text{-diff-pp-pin}}$).

In Figure 6.12, V0$_{de\_m}$ is the measured value of voltage. The error estimates between the measured and the theoretical value (all values differential) are given by the following expressions in Equations 6.5 and 6.6.

---

**Equation 6.5** Minimum Error (%)

$$V_{err\_min}(\%) = ([\text{Min}(V0\_{de\_m}) - V0\_{de}]/V0\_{de}) \times 100$$

---

**Equation 6.6** Maximum Error (%)

$$V_{err\_max}(\%) = ([\text{Max}(V0\_{de\_m}) - V0\_{de}]/V0\_{de}) \times 100$$

---

The errors in the equalization levels comprise errors from resolution of current sources, nonlinearity in current sources, terminations, and aging, among other factors.

The choice of $x$ dB of equalization depends on the designed range and the most likely magnitudes to be employed. The complete range of equalization a device supports and granularity of adjustment is dependent on the product's expected full range of link topologies (loss) to operate within, as determined by an electrical full link analysis. During testing, users should choose several different equalization settings to validate the functionality, but it is not required to exhaustively check all combinations.

*Reference Clock Specifications*

All of the reference clock specifications are common specifications. For all current Intel QPI platforms and components, the reference clock requirements are the same. Within a clock domain, which comprises all components that share one or more Intel QPI links, all of the reference clocks originate from a single clock source. The individual component reference clock inputs must have the same reference clock frequency. If there are many components, the clock may be buffered, but the frequency must not be altered.

The clock specifications are validated in a topology as shown in Figure 6.13. The validation probe at the end of the link (illustrated as a "5" on a die to represent a SMA or SMP type connection footprint) needs to be high impedance. Vendor specifications for the exact values of the capacitors and series resistors need to be followed. The pull-down resistors are 50 ohm (as also defined for system implementations, where these are to be placed at the receiving component inputs).

The real time scope to be used for this purpose, for example, may be either Agilent[†] DSO81204A (12 GHz) or Tektronix[†] 6154 (13–15 GHz) or any other vendor oscilloscope, with at least 12 GHz bandwidth, 2 MB of buffer memory and 40 GS/s on at least two channels. These instruments are specified for validation in order to utilize the large memory buffers available in these machines. If the available memory is not sufficient to complete these tests, repeated measurements should be made and the results cascaded.

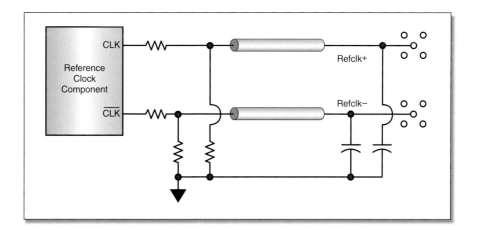

**Figure 6.13** Reference Clock Validation Setup

The reference clock is a differential signal, but some specifications are validated differentially while others are validated either converted to a single-ended signal or by the Refclk+ and Refclk- individually as single-ended signals.

The specifications that are validated as single-ended signals include $V_{Refclk\_min}$, $V_{Refclk\_max}$, $V_{cross}$, and $V_{cross\_delta}$ as shown in Figure 6.14. Each of these specifications is measured over 100,000 clock cycles, which can be collected using infinite persistence mode. Spread spectrum clocking (SSC) should be enabled for these measurements.

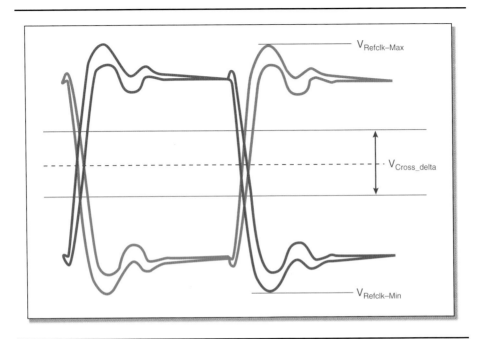

**Figure 6.14** Reference Clock Single-ended Voltage Margin

For the $V_{Refclk\_min}$ the lowest voltage point should be recorded and for $V_{Refclk\_max}$ the highest voltage point should be recorded. For the $V_{cross}$ measurement, the minimum and maximum single-ended crossing points are to be within the range specified. For the $V_{cross\_delta}$, the difference between the minimum and maximum crossing variation must be within a specified value.

The differentially validated specifications include refclk frequency ($f_{Refclk}$), rise/fall time ($ER_{Refclk-diffRise}$, $ER_{Refclk-diffFall}$), duty cycle ($T_{Refclk-Dutycycle}$), differential input high and low voltage ($V_{Refclk\_diff-ih}$, $V_{Refclk\_diff-il}$), and refclk jitter ($T_{Refclk-jitter-rms-onepll}$). Some of these differential specifications are depicted in Figure 6.14. There is one other reference clock specification, $T_{Refclk-diff-jit}$, which actually specifies the long-term signal phase drift, so is covered in the following section with the other data/clock skew specifications.

Each of these specifications is measured over 100,000 clock cycles, except $T_{Refclk-diff-jit}$, which is measured over 50,000 clock cycles. For $f_{Refclk}$, and duty cycle measurements, the SSC must be turned off. For all of the other specs, SSC is on.

For $f_{Refclk}$, the Refclk+ and Refclk- signals may either be measured as one differential signal, or measured separately. The average period over the 100,000 cycles must be within the specified range.

For the rise and fall time measurements ($ER_{Refclk-diffRise}$, $ER_{Refclk-diffFall}$), combine the Refclk+ and Refclk- into one differential waveform, and measure the rise and fall time between the -150 mV and +150 mV crossing points. For the input voltage high and low measurements, the minimum voltage (for $V_{Refclk\_diff-ih}$) and maximum voltage (for $V_{Refclk\_diff-il}$) are recorded after the signals pass beyond 150 mV from the 0V. As seen in Figure 6.15, the worst-case values recorded may be due to signal ringback from overshoot.

The reference clock jitter ($T_{Refclk-jitter-rms-onepll}$) is the accumulated RMS jitter at the reference clock input. This jitter is accumulated over N UI, in which N is values from 1 through 12. The reference clock is collected over 50,000 cycles and the cases of N=1, N=2, ..., N=12 consecutive UIs are convolved through the specified PLL transfer function as shown in Equation 6.7:

**Equation 6.7** PLL Transfer Function to Compute Reference Clock Jitter

$$H(s) = 2 \ \zeta \ w_n s + w_n^2 / (s^2 + 2\zeta w_n s + w_n^2)$$

In this equation, the underdamping factor $\zeta$ is 0.8, natural frequency, $f_n = 7.8E6$ Hz and $w_n = 2\varpi f_n$.

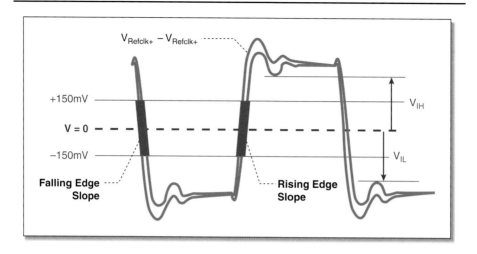

**Figure 6.15** Reference Clock Differential Measurements

*Clock and Data Long-term Phase Drift Specifications*

There are two long-term phase drift specifications. One, mentioned in the reference clock section, is the reference clock drift between any two Intel QPI component reference clock inputs ($T_{Refclk-diff-jit}$). The other is the phase drift between each component's reference clock input and the Tx signals at the transmitter output pin ($T_{Refclk-Tx-Variability}$). Both of these drift specs are illustrated below in Figure 6.16.

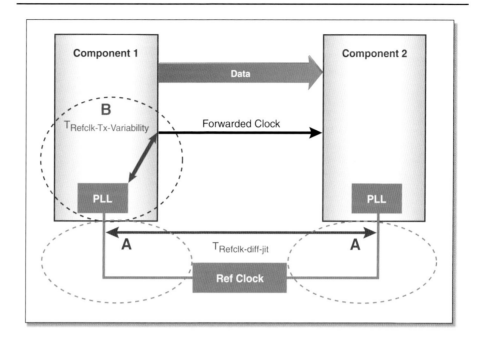

**Figure 6.16** Clock and Tx Phase Drift Specifications

Both of these specifications are intended to limit the long-term drift of the signal phases due to temperature, voltage, humidity, and other factors that may affect the phase. Each drift specification is 500 pS, so the total long-term phase drift allowed between any two connected components is 1 nS, which at 6.4 GT/s is between 6 and 7 UI.

## Platform-dependent Specifications

As mentioned in Chapter 2, the individual specification values vary according to the platform type or data signaling rate. The platform-dependent specifications are defined for both Intel QPI transmitter and receiver specifications.

*Transmitter Parameters*

All transmitter (and transmitter forwarded clock) measurements are made using the test load configuration shown in Figure 6.17. The intent is to measure the parameter values as close to the transmitter output pin as possible. Ideally, the measurements would be made at the output pins themselves, but this is not always possible. If the measurements are made at a point away from the output pins, the validator should consider characterizing the effect of the additional trace, via or other element to subtract (de-embed) it from the measurement.

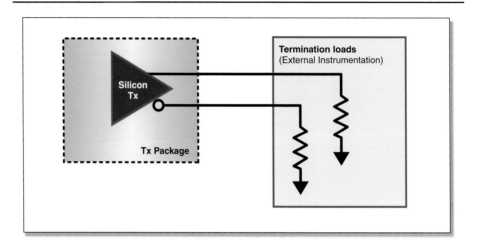

**Figure 6.17** Tx (Data or Forwarded Clock) Validation Setup

The transmitter platform-dependent parameters, shown in Figure 6.18, include those that are only measured at the transmitter, but not the receiver. Some specification parameters have a counterpart at the receiver (for example DC and AC common mode voltage), and yet are not measured at the receiver, but instead are forced for receiver margining tests. One parameter that is measured both at the transmitter and receiver is the data to forwarded clock skew, which will be covered after the transmitter-only parameters.

The transmitter-only measured parameters are:

■ Transmitter differential output voltage swing ($V_{Tx\text{-}diff\text{-}pp\text{-}pin}$)

■ Duty cycle ($TX_{duty\text{-}pin}$)

■ Low (on) transmitter impedance ($Z_{TX\text{-}LOW\text{-}CM\text{-}DC}$)

■ DC common mode voltage ($V_{Tx\text{-}cm\text{-}dc\text{-}pin}$)

■ AC common mode voltage ($V_{Tx\text{-}cm\text{-}ac\text{-}pin}$)

■ Jitter ($TX_{jitUItoUI\text{-}1E\text{-}7\text{-}pin}$, $TX_{jitUItoUI\text{-}1E\text{-}9\text{-}pin}$, $TX_{clk\text{-}acc\text{-}jit\text{-}N\_UI}$)

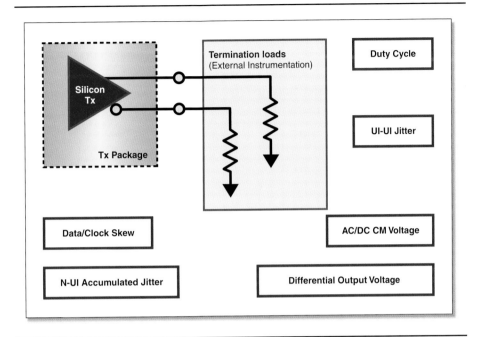

**Figure 6.18** Transmitter Parameters

## Tx Differential Voltage Swing

The transmitter output signal measurement is specified into the impedance of the receiver termination, which has a range of impedance as defined by the specific platform requirements. Ultimately, the transmitter will be driving into the impedance of the package and interconnect elements as well (in-system) are intended to match the platform-dependent termination range. The measurement equipment, however, will most likely not match the specified impedance range, and will instead be about 50 ohms. The measurements made will need to de-embed the termination impedance difference to account for this difference.

For all data lanes, the transmitter is to send out slow, periodic data patterns at frequencies of f/40, f/80, and f/120, where *f* is the full speed of the link (corresponding to 101010…). For each of these frequencies, collect the waveforms in a real-time scope and measure the minimum value of the opening at the center of the eye (0.5UI) of the pattern. The loss due to package trace and the scope noise floor need to be de-embedded to arrive at the differential swing at the transmitter pad.

For the clock lane, the transmitter is to send out the clock pattern at the operational frequency (f) instead of the lower frequencies for the data. As with the data signals, extrapolate the transmitter swing to the pad by de-embedding the AC package loss and the scope noise floor.

The errors to account for during the measurement and post-processing of the measurement data are reference termination difference error, package trace low frequency loss estimation error, and measurement errors.

### Tx Duty Cycle

This specification is measured similar to the UI-UI jitter measurements. Transmit the clock pattern at operational speed (101010…) and collect $N_{MIN-UI-Validation}$ UI samples. The first step is to determine the duty cycle distortion (DCD). The transmitter duty cycle ($TX_{duty-pin}$) is defined as $2 \times UI$ DCD. Due to static duty cycle error and many deterministic dynamic jitters (Dj), the UI-UI jitter and DCD distributions have bi-modal peaks.

TO compute the UI DCD, separate all of the odd UI measurements into one group and the even UI measurements into a separate group. Compute the magnitude of the $UI_{avg}$ – average($UI_{odd}$) and the $UI_{avg}$ – average($UI_{even}$), and the UI-UI DCD is equal to 2 times the UI DCD computed.

### Tx Low (on) Transmitter Impedance

Validation of this specification was described in the termination specification validation section earlier.

### Tx DC Common Mode Voltage

The transmitter DC common mode voltage specification ($V_{Tx-cm-dc-pin}$) is the long-term average DC voltage at operational frequency (f). Random and worst-case data patterns should be generated for the data samples. For each data lane, the D+ and D- signals need to be measured individually as single-ended signals. At least 10 samples of $N_{MIN\_UI-Validation}$ UI need to be collected with the DC common mode voltage computed for all samples.

### Tx AC Common Mode Voltage

The AC common mode voltage ($V_{TX-cm-ac-pin}$) data collection uses the same data patterns and data collection procedure as for $V_{TX-cm-dc-pin}$. As is the DC common mode voltage, the AC common mode voltage is a single-peak profile as shown in Figure 6.19. The resultant AC common model voltage is computed by subtracting the scope noise floor.

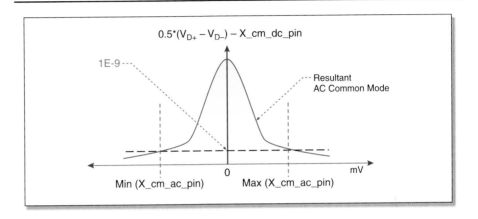

**Figure 6.19** AC Common Mode Voltage Profile

*Tx Jitter Parameters*

The transmitter output jitter specifications include UI-UI jitter ($TX_{jitUI-UI-1E-7pin}$, $TX_{jitUI-UI-1E-9pin}$) and accumulated jitter ($TX_{clk-acc-jit-N\_UI-1E-7}$, $TX_{clk-acc-jit-N\_UI-1E-9}$). These jitter measurements are made at the transmitter output pin. The UI-UI jitter and accumulated jitter are measured on both the data and forwarded clock lanes.

Intel QPI jitter specifications are listed for two bit error rates: $1x10^{-7}$ and $1x10^{-9}$. These bit error rate parameters are measured instead of a direct $1x10^{-14}$ for two reasons. One is a limitation of oscilloscope memory, which does not have the capacity to record data for one sampling run of consecutive UI to directly collect the required data. The other reason is that the time to collect the number of UI (more than $10^{14}$ UI) is greater than 4 hours at 6.4 GT/s (and longer for lower data rates).

Since the measurements are made at $10^7$ and $10^9$ UI sample levels and not $10^{14}$, the $1x10^{-14}$ BER performance is estimated by tail-fitting extrapolation from the $10^7$ and $10^9$ sample size measurements. As seen in Figure 6.20, if the eye width (horizontal point separation) measurement is made at $10^7$ UI samples, the extrapolation of the bit error rate to $1 \times 10^{-14}$ has a much wider range of predicted BER than if the measurement is done at $10^9$ samples. The purple shaded region is the extrapolation uncertainty at $10^7$ samples, and the blue shaded region is the uncertainty at $10^9$ samples. Note that the extrapolation uncertainty is much less when sampling at $10^9$ UI samples. To allow for better accuracy in extrapolating the measured data to the $1 \times 10^{-14}$ BER, a specification of percentage UI jitter at BOTH $10^7$ and $10^9$ provides the basis to perform better tail-fitting.

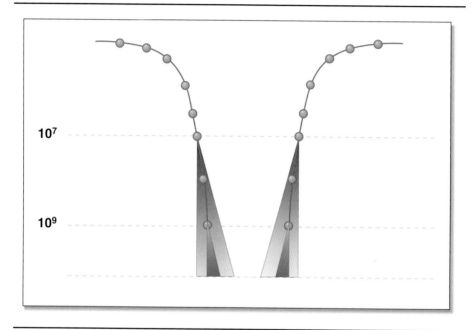

**Figure 6.20** Jitter Accuracy versus Samples

For the UI-UI specs ($\text{TX}_{\text{jitUI-UI-1E-7pin}}$, $\text{TX}_{\text{jitUI-UI-1E-9pin}}$), a clock pattern (101010…) is transmitted at the operational frequency (f) on the data lanes. Every UI timing width needs to be measured by collecting the required number of data samples (differential) in one triggering of the oscilloscope. For $10^{-7}$, at least 100,000,000 ($10^8$) samples are collected. For $10^{-9}$, at least 1,000,000,000 ($10^9$) samples are collected. Six sets of samples need to be collected for each individual data and clock lane, and analyzed separately. Each consecutive pair of UI ($\text{UI}_1$-$\text{UI}_2$, $\text{UI}_2$-$\text{UI}_3$, … $\text{UI}_{N-1}$, $\text{UI}_N$) needs to be measured for the timing difference and composite distribution.

With the transmitter in compliance mode, the individual transmit lane under test is generating the clock pattern, while all other transmitters are generating a pseudo-random bit sequence (PRBS) pattern to trigger an aggravated crosstalk and switching noise condition.

Compute the probability of different points in the tail of the distribution (the number of occurrences within the total number of UI), and ensure that the probability of all points greater than the specification is less than the specified BER as in Figure 6.21. For $10^{-7}$, the points are denoted as "B" and for $10^{-9}$, the points are denoted as "C". Also note that the jitter distribution will typically be bi-modal, with the two peaks caused by duty cycle distortion.

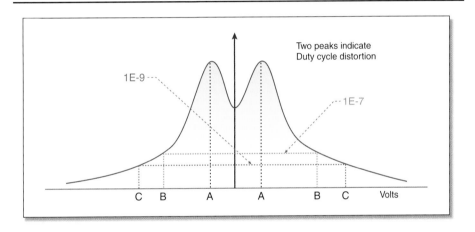

**Figure 6.21** Jitter Profile

For the N-UI jitter specs ($TX_{clk-acc-jit-N\_UI-1E-7}$, $TX_{clk-acc-jit-N\_UI-1E-9}$), a clock pattern (101010…) is transmitted at the operational frequency (f) on the data lanes. The peak-to-peak accumulated jitter is computed for consecutive groupings of UI between 1UI to 12UI (including the numbers between 1 and 12). Each consecutive grouping of UI is to be checked for p-p jitter as a slice swept across the data record. The data and clock patterns and conditions for the transmitter and receiver lanes are the same as for the UI-UI jitter measurements.

*Tx and Rx Data to Forward Clock Skew*

The data to forwarded clock skew applies to both the transmitter and receiver pins. The intent is to limit the maximum skew at the transmitter due to silicon and package design, and to limit the skew but provide PCB signal trace routing flexibility to the receiver as shown in Figure 6.22. The transmitter clock to data skew is a smaller range than the receiver clock to data skew range, which makes sense since the PCB routing can only add to the signal timing uncertainty and is intended to provide some routing relaxation.

For the transmitter data to clock skew ($T_{Tx\text{-}data\text{-}clk\text{-}skew\text{-}pin}$), the clock and data lane under test (testing the clock and one data lane at a time) both generate a 101010… pattern at operational speed. The measurements are to be made over $N_{MIN\text{-}UI\text{-}Validation}$ UI with no SSC. Measure the phase skew between the data and clock lane for each UI and plot the histogram. The peaks of the histogram represent the phase skew.

This measurement needs to be performed for the forwarded clock and all data lanes. These measurements need to be repeated for configurations that may use one or both of the alternate forwarded clocks.

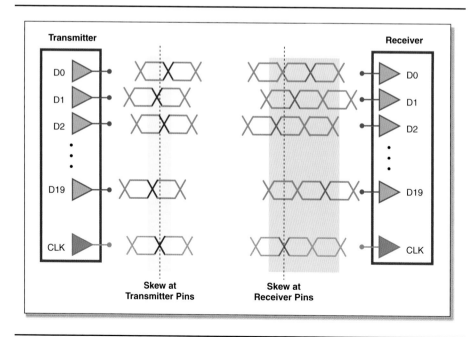

**Figure 6.22** Intel® QuickPath Interconnect Tx and Rx Data to Forwarded Clock Skew

For the receiver data to clock skew ($T_{Rx-data-clk-skew-pin}$), this specification needs to be measured in a system-like topology at the receiver input pin using a high-impedance probe (for example, with the Intel QPI load board, as described later in this chapter).

*Receiver Margining*

Most of the receiver specification parameters are not directly measurable, since the required performance is not at the pin, but at the receiver pad or determined by the receiver response inside the input structure. In addition there are some receiver parameters that are not measured, but are instead forced at the receiver input so that the receiver performance may be tested, or margined to these specification conditions. Of course, the source of the signal input at the receiver must be calibrated beforehand.

The reason that some of the receiver specifications are at the pad and not at the pin is that measurements that are made at the receiver pin are subject to either measurement load interference or package load effects due to impedance mismatch and reflections. The signal measured at the pin may be amplified or diminished, which also is impacted by the data pattern. So, to effectively validate the receiver signal sensitivity, indirect validation methods are employed through receiver margining tests.

Unlike the transmitter, the receiver doesn't have explicit outputs which can be measured by a scope. The performance of the receiver needs to be validated using a specified set of inputs. Whereas there may be some internal signal observation points inside the component that could be logically accessed, it is not an Intel QPI requirement to multiplex any internal signals or nodes for external signal observation. Individual component designs may design their own debug and validation hooks to provide this capability, but the specification does not require it.

The receiver specifications include two types of parameters: margined and forced. The margined parameters are checked to test performance to specified (margined) values. The forced parameters are provided as receiver input conditions and applied for some of the margining parameter tests. The receiver specification parameters are described in Chapter 2, and identified here for validation as to whether a forced or margined parameter:

- $V_{\text{Rx-vmargin}}$ (margined)
- $T_{\text{Rx-tmargn}}$ (margined)
- $T_{\text{Rx-margin}}$ (margined)
- $V_{\text{Rx-margin}}$ (margined)
- $V_{\text{Rx-clk}}$ (margined)
- $T_{\text{Rx-margin-RxEQ}}$ (margined)
- $V_{\text{Rx-margin-RxEQ}}$ (margined)
- $V_{\text{Rx-cm-dc-pin}}$ (forced)
- $V_{\text{Rx-cm-ac-pin}}$ (forced)
- $T_{\text{Rx-DCD-CLK}}$ (forced)

The validation of the receiver uses methods that are also used for board-level receiver testing. The difference between the component and board testing is that much of this detail is not needed for the board-level testing because there are tools (Intel IBIST) to automate much of this for customers of Intel components. The details are provided to illustrate the comprehensive scope of receiver validation, of which board-level validation is a subset.

The receiver should first be calibrated and measured using a dedicated instrument that can inject a defined pattern with a controlled amount of jitter and noise, as shown in Figure 6.7. The validation test then needs to measure the amount of timing margin that exists inside the receiver. This measurement can be done using a BERT that can act as the external signal and pattern generator and also receive the received pattern back to the BERT through a loopback to do error comparison and bit error rate estimates: refer to Figure 6.23.

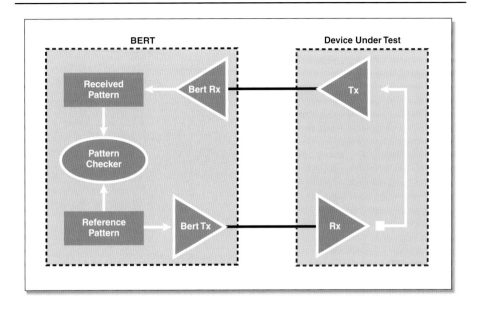

**Figure 6.23** BERT Loopback with Error Comparison

*Setup for BERT Controlled Receiver Margining*

A schematic of the recommended BERT setup is shown in Figure 6.24. Note that the BERT provides (a) the reference clock, which is set to a fixed ratio of the forwarded clock and may inject spread-spectrum clocking (SSC) downspreading as per the specification, (b) forwarded clock, (c) transmit data, and (d) receive data inputs.

The BERT may be attached close to the DUT for the transmitted signals, or may have a stressed interconnect channel to emphasize some real channel behavior. However, the BERT receive data inputs should always be connected as close to the DUT transmitters so as to not introduce bit errors from the transmitter channel back to the BERT.

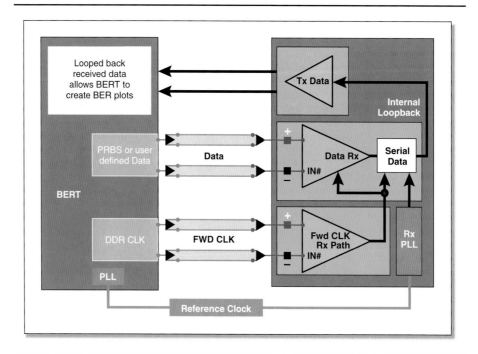

**Figure 6.24** BERT Detailed Setup

The BERT must be able to:

■ Send a compatible differential forwarded clock while sending a user controlled data pattern (with or without PRBS) at multiple applicable controlled voltage levels.

■ Inject user-controlled jitter into the data and variable limited jitter into the forwarded clock outputs.

■ Generate an appropriately divided reference clock from the main forwarded clock that can be supplied to the receiver to drive the receiver PLL.

■ Have a versatile clock data recovery (CDR) loop to receive the looped-back transmitter data, with the bandwidth of the CDR being high enough to integrate most of the noise added in the internal loopback path after the data receiver amplifier.

■ Generate a user-controlled delay between the data and forwarded clock outputs with fine granularity (100 femtoseconds).

In addition, the BERT should also have available the following hardware:

■ A transmitter de-emphasis block, preferably multi-tap. Its usage may be to correlate and assess margins with transmitter equalization-only operation.

■ Accessories such as a bias-T for DC common-mode shifting of outputs. Amplifiers, attenuators and signal generators for AC common-mode noise injection.

■ Transition time converters to be connected right after the BERT Tx outputs of data and forwarded clock, which serve to reduce the sharp rise/fall times. This not only helps minimize reflections but also is necessary for inducing the differential waveform's duty cycle distortion by selectively level-shifting DC common modes of the output+ versus output- signals.

■ Optionally to counter the loss related to intersymbol interference (ISI) due to package effects, a transmitter equalizer (which is usually an external unit coupled to the data output of the BERT) can be used.

*Receiver Margining Tests*

There are multiple types of receiver margining tests to run to comprehensively characterize the receiver performance and margins. The board and platform designer will test the receiver sensitivity with tools enabled by Intel, so will not need to be setting up the tests at this level of detail that the component validator will. For each test, the DUT receiver needs to first be initialized by putting it through compliance.loopback or loopback.slave mode, as discussed earlier. Thereafter the BERT will inject some specific data patterns with a given set of jitter, AC and DC common mode voltage conditions and then receive the looped back data patterns back under no data-clock delay. For margining tests that involve timing margin validation, the forwarded clock delay (relative to the data phase) has to be swept over a complete UI, recording the bit error rate out of the BERT for every setting of the delay. Due to random variations, the bit error rate needs be averaged over many thousands of UI, in order to create a relatively smooth BER versus voltage offset or BER versus data-clock phase delay plots.

The receiver margining tests are divided into simple pattern-based tests and complex, nonperiodic pattern-based tests. The simple pattern-based tests need to be completed prior to performing the complex, nonperiodic pattern-based tests. Once the simple tests are completed passing with required margins, the absence of silicon-related issues allows the more complex pattern-based tests to be conducted.

The simple pattern-based tests consist of repetitive patterns of varying frequency, with no injected jitter and are primarily meant to test the intrinsic silicon characteristics (avoiding or minimizing the ISI and crosstalk from the package, socket, and PCB). The tests include:

- Receiver forwarded clock path voltage sensitivity
- Receiver data lane voltage sensitivity
- Receiver data lane timing sensitivity

The complex nonperiodic pattern-based tests are then performed for voltage and timing margin sensitivity. The pattern used is a specific PRBS pattern, PRBS-31. These tests involve sending this pseudo-random pattern with jitter injection from the BERT. This in turn invokes additional circuit and signal integrity deterioration responses such as ISI and random jitter amplification on the data lanes and reveals receiver data pattern sensitivities. In addition to the interconnect path and receiver design complexity, the test environment introduces other effects that may be difficult to determine the individual parameter effects on the receiver behavior. One simple example of this is the test environment impedance (50 ohm) versus the Intel QPI component terminations (closer to 42 ohms).

Even though receiver-based equalization is not required for Intel QPI, some designs may decide to include it in their receiver designs. The complex PRBS-31 pattern testing is also used for equalization-based designs by comparing margined results with equalization employed and not present.

### Receiver Forwarded Clock Voltage Margining Tests

This test is a measure of voltage sensitivity of the forwarded clock receiver. This is a component-level margining test that does not need to be performed by the board or platform validator. In order to perform this test, the forwarded clock input needs to be subjected to a 1010… pattern of varying magnitude and using the BERT setup, checked for the looped back data (on any lane) when the data input is a periodic pattern without injected jitter. The forwarded clock input voltage swing should be started as a large magnitude (such as 800 mV differential) and the whole BERT setup completed to align the sampling clock at the and loopback data received without error. Thereafter the amplitude of the forwarded clock (as measured at the forwarded clock input pin) should be slowly reduced till the looped back data suddenly starts recording a large number of errors as illustrated in Figure 6.25. This test should be repeated by creating a duty cycle distortion in the input clock by level shifting the CLKIN and CLKIN# with respect to each other (when the input waveforms are sinusoidal like). Alternately this testing can also be done by observing the sampling clock through an observation or on-die probing mechanism. It should be ensured that the minimum specification amplitude values for VRx-CLK and resilience against a maximum applied UI DCD of TRx-DCD-CLK is adhered to, simultaneously.

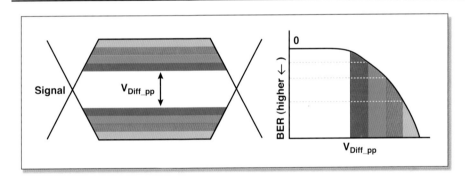

**Figure 6.25** BER versus Voltage Margining

Note that no dynamic jitter is applied at the forwarded clock receiver input for this testing. However every design effort should be applied for minimizing random jitter amplification of the design receiver forwarded clock path.

*Receiver Data Lane Voltage Margining Tests*

This test is a measure of voltage sensitivity of any one of the data lanes of the receiver. This is a component-level margining test that does not need to be performed by the board or platform validator. This test measures the bit error rate versus the input differential voltage, when the sampling clock is best aligned, to the center of the data pattern. The input data pattern is a periodic (repeating) pattern of varying frequency, including a 1010... pattern. This test is to be performed on an individual lane, one at a time, so that cross-talk is not corrupting the observations. The purpose of specifying a periodic pattern and doing individual lane testing is to decouple (or de-embed) package/socket induced ISI and crosstalk. The insertion loss of the short PCB trace and the package trace cannot be avoided and neither can the impedance difference of the instrument versus the receiver terminations, which therefore need to be measured or estimated and subtracted out, when plotting the bit error rate against the applied differential voltage.

The input data patterns used should range from repeating 32 "1" to 32 "0" to 1010.... The sensitivity testing should be done starting from the slowest repeating patterns to the fastest one (that is, 1010...), and the specified bit error rate should be satisfied for the value of the input voltage, after accounting for package/socket/PCB trace loss and the instrument-Rx termination impedance difference.

All other lanes of the receiver and the transmitter (other than the looped back lane) need to be excited with some random patterns in order to generate a regular system like power grid voltage noise; however, this testing should be done in such a way as to not be corrupted by package/socket crosstalk. The objective here is to also test the receiver sensitivity to on-die power grid noise.

As long as the forwarded clock sensitivity testing has been performed, the forwarded clock input amplitude can be maintained at ~1.5 × $V_{Rx\text{-}CLK}$ and the CLK duty cycle distortion maintained at $T_{Rx\text{-}DCD\text{-}CLK}$, during this testing. It is expected that the forwarded clock lane has enough duty cycle correction, to be robust against this DCD.

The bit error rate versus input voltage sensitivity curve to be measured for each of the patterns, similar to the clock case, is shown in Figure 6.25. One can simplify measurements by measuring at the lowest frequency (32 "1" and 32 "0") and at the highest frequency (1010...) and ensuring that both of these measurements satisfy the specification, in which case it can be safely assumed that the intermediate frequencies will also satisfy the specification. However this assumption can be in question if there is a package resonance or any pattern dependent noise, so users need to check validity of assumptions.

Note that the complete BER curve versus applied input differential voltage is not specified. The curve can have different shapes depending on the fraction on deterministic noise and random noise. It is assumed that off-set cancellation is done to the best extent possible and the curve is measured multiple times for repeatability.

For all the measurements, the sampling clock for the receiver needs to aligned and kept aligned at the most optimum position. Measurement of sensitivity for the 1010... pattern therefore needs to be done with care, since this data will be most affected by misalignment among all data pattern frequencies.

The measurement should be done by slowly reducing the input differential voltage and moving to finer voltage granularities and performing averaging of the bit error rate (a degree of averaging that smoothes out the measurements). The measurement should be repeated by interchanging Data IN and Data IN# inputs, so that any residual offset effects can be comprehended.

*Receiver Data Lane Timing Margining Tests*

This test should be done after the forwarded clock lane and the data lane voltage sensitivity tests are completed. This is a component-level margining test that does not need to be performed by the board or platform validator. The forwarded clock is phase shifted from the input data, after initial clock alignment for this testing, to plot the bit error rate versus the phase shifts (with +/- 0.5 UI of the clock alignment position). The input data pattern applied is a slow periodic pattern with no external jitter. All other lanes of the receiver and the transmitter need to be excited with some random patterns in order to generate a regular system like power grid voltage noise, however this testing should be done in a manner not to be corrupted by package/socket crosstalk. The objective here is to also test the receiver sensitivity to on-die power grid noise that can influence the sampling clock and the data receiver.

The complete BER curve shape versus applied data-clock phase shift is not specified. The curve can have different shapes depending on the fraction of deterministic jitter (Dj) and random jitter (Rj) within the receiver and will be of the form shown in Figure 6.26.

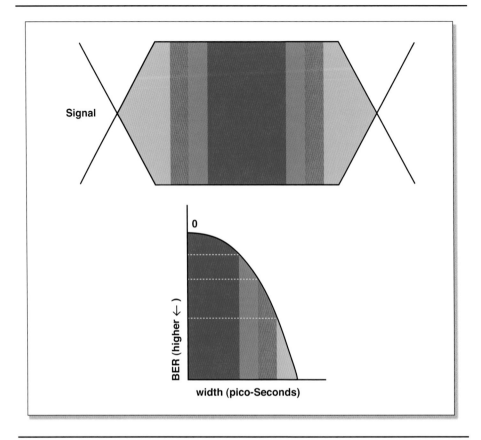

**Figure 6.26** BER versus Timing Margining)

As long as the forwarded clock sensitivity testing has been performed, the forwarded clock input amplitude can be maintained at 500 mV differential peak-to-peak and the clock duty cycle distortion maintained at $T_{Rx\text{-}DCD\text{-}CLK}$ during this testing. It is expected that the forwarded clock lane has enough duty cycle correction to be robust against this DCD. The input data patterns used, should range from a consecutive set of 32 "1" to 32 "0" UI, to four "1" and four "0" UI.

Since the clock is phase-shifted with respect to the data lane to map out the internal timing margin, the test is a measure of receiver internal jitter and does not measure clock placement errors or slow drift. Since the forwarded clock signal applied is clean other than duty cycle distortion (due to equipment limitations), this test does not measure the forwarded clock path jitter amplification either. Other link margining tests would be needed to assess these jitter parameters.

### Receiver Complex Pattern (PRBS-31) Margining Tests

This testing needs to be done once the receiver has passed simple pattern-based testing of the data path and the forwarded clock receiver. This is because the PRBS pattern-based testing is subject to signal integrity degradation from ISI effects from test fixtures and the whole connection between the instrument and the data input. There may be impedance mismatches between 50 ohms to the target impedances of package and Rx terminations and additional effects that may not exist in a system like environment but do exist in the testing environment. Therefore this test employs a relatively gentle input conditions and failure of this test can be indicative of test setup issues that need to be checked first before checking any pattern-dependent effects inside the silicon.

### Setting Up Input Conditions for Random Pattern Based Testing

The BERT used for testing should be programmed to send PRBS-31 pattern with appropriately calibrated injected jitter from the BERT transmitter. The injected jitter should be a mixture of PRBS jitter, sinusoidal jitter and Gaussian random jitter.

The BERT output should be looped back to itself to check the input eye for the parameters $V_{Rx-input}$ and $T_{Rx-input}$. Once the PRBS and Gaussian jitters are maximized, the sinusoidal jitter magnitude should be adjusted along with adjustment of voltage amplitude, to get the correct $T_{Rx-input}$ and $V_{Rx-input}$. The conditions to be imposed at the input to the receiver are specified in Table 6.1.

**Table 6.1**  Receiver Margining Input Parameters

| Symbol | Parameter |
|---|---|
| $T_{Rx\text{-}Gaussian}$ | Gaussian UI jitter calibrated and measured using a 1010... pattern out of BERT Tx |
| $T_{Rx\text{-}Prbs}$ | Deterministic PRBS pattern like ISI jitter, calibrated and measured using a 1010... pattern out of BERT Tx |
| $T_{Rx\text{-}sin}$ | Peak-to-peak sinusoidal jitter injected from BERT Tx |
| $T_{Rx\text{-}DCD\text{-}CLK}$ | Duty cycle distortion as applied to the input forwarded CLK |
| $V_{Rx\text{-}CLK}$ | Voltage eye opening of forwarded clock signal out of BERT |
| $V_{Rx\text{-}min\text{-}max\text{-}ratio}$ | Max/Min pulse voltage ratio seen between two consecutive UI |
| $V_{Rx\text{-}input}$ | Maximum differential voltage eye opening to be imposed at the input to the receiver |
| $T_{Rx\text{-}input}$ | Maximum timing eye opening for the differential measurement to be imposed at the input to the receiver |

### Timing and Voltage Margining of Rx with Random Pattern

Once the random pattern is being received and looped back correctly with all the input conditions specified, the sampling clock should be aligned properly either through a regular bit-locking process or manually. Thereafter the phase delay of the clock should be swept relative to the data. The bit error rate versus delay curve is plotted the same manner as for the receiver data lane timing margin tests as depicted in Figure 6.26, which shows the expected shape of receiver timing margin versus BER (cumulative error probability).

The BERT should be capable of receiving the returned data output out of the Intel QPI receiver and align to it using its own internal clock and receiver, so that it can do the BER recording, comparing the data sent to the data received (refer to Figure 6.23). Since the BERT is recording the bit error rates, the lowest value of BER that the user can measure depends on the speed at which this validation is done. If the measurements do not go down to 1E-14, the measured BER profile needs to be extrapolated using a tail fitting procedure to get the timing margin at $1 \times 10^{-14}$. In order to avoid extrapolation errors, the measurement needs to be extended as close to $1 \times 10^{-14}$ as possible.

Since all the transmitters are in loopback mode, one needs to connect PRBS sources at the inputs to as many receivers as possible to make the Tx-Rx pairs generate and receive random data patterns.

*Margining of Receivers with Receiver Equalization*

Receiver equalization is not required for Intel QPI, but it is allowed. Some components that are designed for use in platforms "pushing the envelope," for example two-connector, three-board topologies, may add extra receiver-based equalization to amplify the received signal. The input specifications for receivers with equalization are the same as for receivers with no equalization. In order to validate the performance of receiver equalization, receiver margining measurements need to use PRBS-like patterns with ISI. This is due to the BERT to receiver input path frequency-dependent loss. Also, some other configuration and task steps need to be followed to validate the receiver equalization performance:

■ The optional transmitter equalizer connected to BERT data transmitter output needs to be disconnected.

■ The timing margins must be measured using receiver equalization off and receiver equalization coefficients on and swept over their required ranges. The user needs to determine the settings of the receiver equalizer that maximizes the measured timing margin.

■ Voltage margins should be measured by adjusting the input amplitude of the signal, at a nominal data-clock delay setting. The voltage margins should be measured using receiver equalization off and then with receiver equalization coefficients on and swept over their required ranges. The user needs to determine the settings of the receiver equalizer that maximizes the measured timing margin. Note that the equalization settings that are optimal for a platform may be different than the optimal settings for a validation environment.

The voltage margin is expected to follow a similar profile as that for the timing margin. The voltage margin is the amount by which the input differential voltage can be lowered, by keeping the forwarded clock at the optimum position of sampling in the data receiver amplifier before reaching the same BER.

## Platform-based Validation and Measurement

Some platform-based performance measurements can be conducted either on the bare PCB or with one or more components mounted. These measurements are to be applied to simulation models for correlation purposes and to measure signal performance for receive-side signals. Other platform-based measurements (Intel IBIST) are intended to be made with the completed board design and components mounted. These measurements assess the Intel® QPI channel health across manufacturing variation to ensure high-volume health.

### Time-Domain Measurements

For PCB differential and common-mode impedance and propagation delay, time-domain reflectometry, and time-domain transmission are typically used. An oscilloscope with a probe module for TDR/TDT is used for these measurements. The probe module has a fast rise time pulse generator that is launched and measured for its reflection and transmission behavior. The reflection behavior maps the transmission line impedance profile and the transmission behavior maps the propagation velocity of the pulse as shown in Figure 6.27. In this example, a shunt resistor terminates the transmission line, so the TDR illustrates the relative impedance of the transmission line and point at which the pulse reaches the shunt resistor.

The TDT shows the actual delay of the pulse along the transmission line to the shunt resistor. Note that the TDR apparent delay is twice that of the TDT. This is due to the TDR reflected signal received traveling twice the distance (out and back).

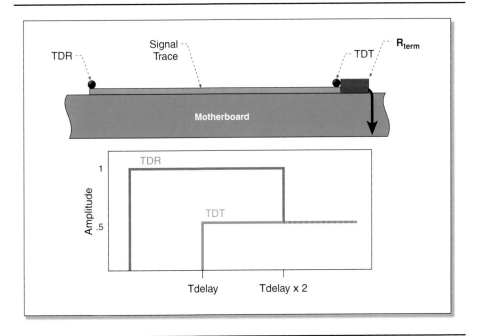

**Figure 6.27** TDR and TDT

## Frequency-Domain Measurements

Another equivalent approach to measuring the PCB trace transmission line behavior is in the frequency domain with a vector network analyzer (VNA). The VNA measures the reflective and transmissive behavior across a range of frequency, so that the trace impedance and phase (propagation velocity) can be profiled for its frequency dependence. A simple 2-port passive device (which could be a signal trace or other passive structure) is shown in Figure 6.28, which highlights the scattering parameters for each port reflection and transmission behavior. Passive components (such as traces, vias, connectors) can be individually measured and characterized this way.

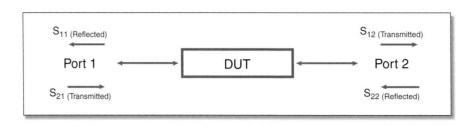

**Figure 6.28** S-parameters

For the input port, the reflected response is S11 and the transmitted response is S12. Similarly, for the output port the reflected response is S21 and the transmitted response is S22.

The VNA is not easy to set up and calibrate, so it should be noted that the time-domain methods of measuring TDR and TDT can also be used to derive the S-parameters.

## Intel® QPI Load Board

The Intel QuickPath Interconnect Load Board (QLB) is a passive test fixture that sits on the CPU socket in place of the processor and enables probing of the forwarded clock and data lanes with predictable signal integrity. The QLB is designed by Intel and is manufactured and sold by Pactron Inc. (ordering information is available directly from Pactron, Inc.). The QLB is different for each CPU, so the QLB needs to be ordered for the specific CPU of interest.

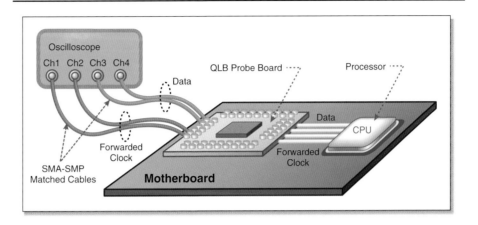

**Figure 6.29** Intel® QuickPath Interconnect Load Board (QLB)

Two pairs of matched SMA-SMP cables are used to connect to the oscilloscope. These should be matched 50 ohm coaxial cables with SMA male connector on one end and SMP female connector on the other end to capture differential data. The cables recommended by Intel are Rosenberger semi-rigid cables P/N 71L-19K1-32S1-01000D.

To reduce voltage loss you can also use 1M SMA(M)-SMA(M) cables with 4" semi-rigid SMA(F)-SMP(F) cables attached to the end of the SMA cables. The Rosenberger part number for the 4" semi-rigid cable is 71L-19K1-32K1-00102C.

## Intel® IBIST Non-Intrusive Margining Testing

In the past, interconnect channel performance didn't rely on BER but rather the measurable size of the eye at the receiver. As data rates have grown beyond 5 GT/s, the discontinuities within the package of the silicon have become a huge impact on the signal itself. What can only be measured at the pin of the device is no longer an accurate representation of what the receiver actually sees at the pad. Even worse, de-embedding the package effects from that signal is growing in complexity, adding theoretical models and simulations to what is supposed to be a measured signal. Instead these "measurements" are now something that is between reality and simulation.

The Intel QPI specifications today insist that the absolute health of any given interconnect channel is its bit error rate. It is difficult and time-consuming to measure anything to the levels that would require finding out the margins of a bus around a BER of $1\times10^{-14}$. Is $5\times10^{-15}$ good enough for a high volume manufacturing scenario? What about $1\times10^{-18}$? And, as was mentioned earlier, nondeterministic or random jitter is the major component in how large the BER is. So how can a designer or a validation engineer know that they have tested well enough to catch the range of failures on their platform?

There is a formula for determining confidence level versus number of bits (UI) sent for any given bus that is measured shown in Equation 6.8. This formula is derived from work found in the industry white paper "Statistical Confidence Levels for Estimating Error Probability" published in *Lightwave* magazine (April 2000).

**Equation 6.8** Formula for Confidence Level versus Number of Bits Measured

$$n = -\ln(1-C)/p - \ln\left(\sum_{k=0}^{N} ((np)k/k!)\right)/p$$

Where:

n = number of bits in a trial

C = confidence level you are trying to obtain

p = probability of failure rate desired (BER)

k = intermediate number of specific errors found in a trial

N = number of errors recorded during this trial

This formula is useful for an individual DUT or case, but doesn't resolve the initial problem of how good a BER must be to cover all the variations that come into play between silicon and platform high volume manufacturing.

Intel IBIST margining tools combine the best of the BER and the eye techniques by obtaining a relative electrical margin on the bus without actually touching the bus with any physical device. These Intel IBIST margining tools have been developed jointly between Intel and ASSET InterTech, Inc. and are a product known as the ScanWorks[†] IBIST Toolkit.

The ScanWorks[†] IBIST Toolkit obtains the electrical margin data by using embedded registers in the receiving silicon itself to vary the electrical sampling thresholds of the receivers both in time and voltage while receiving a known pattern. When at least one bit error is detected on all lanes, the failure is marked in red. If there is a bit error on one or more lanes (but not all), the failure is marked in yellow. If there are no bit errors on all lanes, the sampled case is marked in green denoting a passing result. Once a sampling condition is tested a new electrical sampling threshold is chosen. By this method an entire grid can be plotted not unlike a very, very low speed sampling oscilloscope to develop something akin to the eye of the receiver. Figure 6.30 shows a typical eye diagram generated by the ScanWorks[†] IBIST Toolkit. If the known pattern is complex enough, most of the major contributors to random jitter (ground bounce, crosstalk, voltage droop, and Inter-Symbol Interference [ISI]) can be represented.

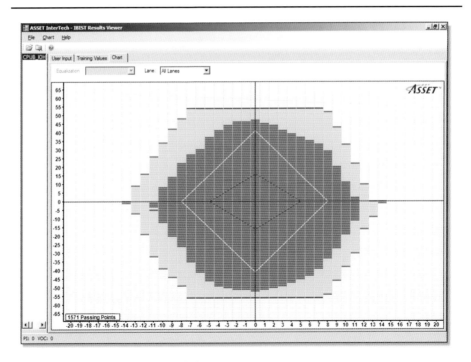

Photo courtesy of ASSET InterTech, Inc.

**Figure 6.30** ScanWorks[†] Generated Eye Diagram

Unfortunately the eye derived is not perfect and can't be immediately correlated to voltage or time due a number of factors including test time (valid BER at Intel QPI speeds take a long time to do thousands of iterations) and variations in the receiver silicon. While this eye is not valid as a direct measure to volts versus picoseconds at the receiver, it is valid to be used within a quantified statistical model. This statistical model, by relatively quick measurements, over just a few systems, allows the user to determine the failure probability of any given platform manufactured using the same interconnect over a given set of known manufacturing skews. The results of this output are expressed in terms of systems per million (SPM). The SPM represents the number of failed systems per million manufactured. This allows the platform validator to make valid risk decisions on the validity of the platform.

The toolkit uses a host PC system, interconnected to the platform under test through a USB cable connecting to the JTAG bus on the target system. All devices connected to that JTAG bus can be controlled through this interface. Figure 6.31 shows a typical host PC and target system configuration.

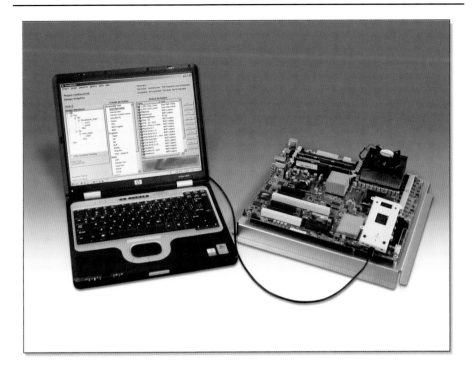

Photo courtesy of ASSET InterTech, Inc.

**Figure 6.31** Typical ScanWorks† IBIST Toolkit Setup

As the methodology for obtaining the raw information is no longer to sample a signal measured in femtoseconds but rather to read and write registers in microseconds over an IEEE 1149.1 JTAG chain, there is a significant advantage in price that the ScanWorks† IBIST Toolkit provides over the 16+GT/s oscilloscopes. Additionally the tests, while individually long, require very little operator intervention allowing one engineer to start a test and then go on about their activities while the day long test runs. Once the data is collected over several of these tests it can be analyzed by Intel into SPM data in just hours. For more information on the ScanWorks† IBIST Toolkit, please see http://www.asset-intertech.com/ or contact ASSET InterTech, Inc. directly.

# Epilogue

The goal of this book is to expand the reader's understanding of the electrical requirements of the Intel® QuickPath Interconnect (Intel QPI). The electrical concepts are applied throughout the design, from timing budgeting, design, modeling, simulation, layout and validation. In addition to this book, you are invited go to this book's companion Web page at http://www.intel.com/intelpress/qpied for a digital edition of the book, training information and live reference links.

The Intel QuickPath Interconnect is the successor to the Front Side Bus (FSB), used in Intel server processors since the Intel® Pentium Pro processor was introduced in 1994. Chapter 1 introduced the historical evolution from multiple processors, I/O devices, and a *single* memory controller on the FSB to the approach used on Intel QPI systems. The Intel QuickPath Interconnect provides a new system foundation which maximizes the potential of future generations of microprocessors.

Intel QPI delivers high bandwidth with a low latency by providing direct high speed links between processors, *multiple* memory controllers, and I/O devices. Multi-processor systems that are fully connected with Intel QPI links offer the lowest latency and can deliver very high performance. All these links operate in parallel providing very high throughput in the system. Such a system also provides improvements over other similar serial interfaces, including PCI Express[†].

In order to understand and effectively apply the electrical specifications, the basic signaling and electrical concepts need to be provided. Chapter 2 explored the basis and definitions of the electrical specifications. Key signal transmission concepts were described to provide a common thread between simulation, layout and validation for the specifications.

Once the electrical specification basics are understood, the high-speed effects of signal transmission through non-ideal, lossy and frequency-dependent interconnects can be combined with the platform components to assess performance impacts. Chapter 3 provided the signal integrity theory apply to the channel components. The loss and jitter impacts as well as transmitter-based equalization to mitigate impact were explained.

To show how to utilize the signal integrity concepts, Chapter 4 applied them to electrical modeling and simulation. Equalization and its benefits were further discussed, as well as the eye diagram requirements and analysis tools provided by Intel to support the Intel QPI interface. As speeds increase, transmitter equalization will most likely be insufficient by itself to ensure respectable signal integrity and positive margins at the receiver. We expect that receive equalization will feature prominently in future at some point, with accompanying tools to support analysis of both equalization types.

Once the timing, signal performance and interconnect channel components are identified, the board-level implantation may be done. Chapter 5 described the rules and guidelines to effectively carry out trace routing and other interconnect channel design elements such as vias and breakout regions. Also, the layer and fiber-weave mitigation considerations were addressed.

Intel QPI allows validation to be done at different levels and with many tools and methods. Capabilities are provided to measure component-level properties as well as interconnect channel characteristics. Chapter 6 described the equipment and measurements to validate Intel QPI. Key concepts and methods were applied to directly validate specifications and test for performance margins.

## Futures

Any modern computer system is designed with upgradability in mind. The Intel Quickpath Interconnect is no different. Both the architecture as a whole as well as the individual layers will allow for expansion and extension. For future applications, with speeds and configurations likely to be much more demanding than today's, this flexibility is crucial.

Our colleagues, in their book *Weaving High Performance Multiprocessor Fabric*, presented a compelling example that the flexibility of Intel QPI extends even to the physical medium used to carry information in a system:

*"For example, the current physical layer of Intel QPI is designed to transfer data over electrical signals, specifically copper wiring on printed circuit boards. This layer is entirely self-contained and in the future could be replaced by one that uses optical media or other suitable high-speed interconnect. The digital and analog sub-blocks of today's physical layer would be redesigned accordingly to take advantage of the capabilities of the new signaling technology. The rest of the layers of the Intel Quickpath Interface, including the messaging content, would be unaffected by such a change."*

While intriguing, these speculations are mere examples of the flexibility and modular design of the architecture. They therefore should not be interpreted in any way to represent the product plans of Intel Corporation.

The Intel QPI architecture permits almost unlimited opportunities for innovation in system configuration. Designers with imagination in a demanding marketplace will have ample room to apply and extend the interface technology in future systems and devices. We wish them all success and will all benefit from their efforts. .

## For More Information

Please visit the Intel Web site, www.intel.com, for the most up-to-date information on all technologies and products offered by Intel that include the Intel QuickPath Interconnect.

# References

Brist, Gary, Stephen Hall, Sidney Clouser and Tao Liang. 2005. "Non-Classical Conductor Losses Due to Copper Foil Roughness and Treatment." *CircuiTree*, May 1, 2005. www.circuitree.com Web site.

Coleman, Dave, Scott Gardiner, Mohammad Kolbehdari, and Stephen Peters. 2004. *PCI Express Electrical Interconnect Design: Practical Solutions for Board-level Integration and Validation*. Hillsboro, OR: Intel Press. www.intel.com/intel-press/sum_pcieh.htm Web site.

Hall, Stephen H., Garrett W. Hall, and James A. McCall. 2000. *High-Speed Digital System Design: A Handbook of Interconnect Theory and Design Practices*. New York, NY: John Wiley & Sons, Inc.

Hall, Stephen, Tao Liang, Howard Heck and David Shykind. 2004. "Modeling Requirements for Transmission Lines in Multi-Gigabit Systems." *IEEE 13th Topical Meeting on Electrical Performance of Electronic Packaging*. Piscataway, NJ: IEEE

Hall, Stephen, Steven G. Pytel, Paul G. Huray, Daniel Hua, Anusha Moonshiram, Gary A. Brist, and Edin Sijercic. 2007. "Multigiahertz Causal Transmission Line Modeling Methodology Using a 3-D Hemispherical Surface Roughess Approach." *IEEE Transactions on Microwave Theory and Techniques,* Vol. 55, No. 12. Piscataway, NJ: IEEE

Hall, Stephen H. and Howard L. Heck. 2009. *Advanced Signal Integrity for High-Speed Digital Designs.* New York, NY: John Wiley & Sons, Inc.

Intel Corporation. 2005. *Intel Higher Education Curriculum Forum: Signal Integrity for High Speed Circuits.* www.intel.com/education/highered/signal/. Santa Clara, CA: Intel Corporation. Web site.

Johnson, Howard and Martin Graham. 1993. *High-Speed Digital Design: A Handbook of Black Magic.* Upper Saddle River, NJ: Prentice Hall.

Johnson, Howard and Martin Graham. 2003. *High-Speed Signal Propagation: Advanced Black Magic.* Upper Saddle River, NJ: Prentice Hall.

Maddox, Robert A., Gurbir Singh and Robert J. Safranek. 2009. *Weaving High Performance Multiprocessor Fabric: Architectural Insights into the Intel® Quick-Path Interconnect* Hillsboro, OR: Intel Press. www.intel.com/intelpress/sum_qpi.htm Web site.

Miller, Dennis. 2004. *Designing High-Speed Interconnect Circuits: Advanced Signal Integrity Methods for Engineers.* OR: Intel Press. www.intel.com/intelpress/sum_mmdi.htm Web site.

Reed, Dana George (ed.). 2001. *The ARRL Handbook for Radio Amateurs.* Newington, CT: ARRL.

Triverio, Piero and Stefano Grivet-Talocia. 2008. "Robust Causality Characterization via Generalized Dispersion Relations." *IEEE Transactions on Advanced Packaging,* Vol. 31, No. 3. Piscataway, NJ: IEEE.

# Index

## Continuing Education is Essential

It's a challenge we all face – keeping pace with constant change in information technology. Whether our formal training was recent or long ago, we must all find time to keep ourselves educated and up to date in spite of the daily time pressures of our profession.

Intel produces technical books to help the industry learn about the latest technologies. The focus of these publications spans the basic motivation and origin for a technology through its practical application.

## Right books, right time, from the experts

These technical books are planned to synchronize with roadmaps for technology and platforms, in order to give the industry a head-start. They provide new insights, in an engineer-to-engineer voice, from named experts. Sharing proven insights and design methods is intended to make it more practical for you to embrace the latest technology with greater design freedom and reduced risks.

I encourage you to take full advantage of Intel Press books as a way to dive deeper into the latest technologies, as you plan and develop your next generation products. They are an essential tool for every practicing engineer or programmer. I hope you will make them a part of your continuing education tool box.

Sincerely,

*Justin Rattner*
*Senior Fellow and Chief Technology Officer*
*Intel Corporation*

*Turn the page to learn about titles*
*from Intel Press for system developers*

(intel®)

# *Weaving High Performance| Multiprocessor Fabric*

## *Architectural insights into the Intel® QuickPath Interconnect*

*By Robert A. Maddox, Gurbir Singh and Robert J. Safranek*
*ISBN 978-1-934053-18-8*

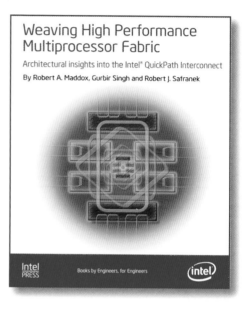

Welcome to the era of the Intel® QuickPath Interconnect!

*Weaving High Performance Multiprocessor Fabric* is written for hardware design, validation and BIOS engineers to introduce the compelling mix of performance and features in the Intel® QuickPath Interconnect. From the Foreword, Robert P. Colwell opines: "Even for inveterate geeks like me, most technical books are dry as dust and work much better than insomnia pills. They should come with warning stickers: Do not operate heavy machinery for a week after reading this book. Not this book though: *Weaving High Performance Multiprocessor Fabric* is engaging, educational, well-organized and directly useful. It doesn't get any better than that."

Sophie Houssiaux of Bull observes: "This book gives a clear view of the concepts, system features and technical details of the Intel® QuickPath Interconnect" which provides the foundation for future generations of Intel® microprocessor systems with a high-speed, packetized, point-to-point system interconnect. It uses multiple narrow high-speed serial links to stitch together processors and IO hubs into a fabric of a distributed shared memory-style platform architecture. The Intel QuickPath Interconnect offers high bandwidth with coherency mechanisms that are optimized for low latency and high scalability, as well as packet and lane structures enabling quick completions of transactions. Reliability, availability, and serviceability features are built into the architecture to satisfy the needs of most mission-critical servers. "With one day of reading this book, everyone familiar with the existing Front Side Bus architecture will have good visibility into what is new in the Intel® QuickPath Interconnect." - Simon Czermak - Fujitsu Siemens Computers Ltd.

# *Active Platform Management Demystified*

## *Unleashing the power of Intel® vPro™ Technology*

*By Arvind Kumar, Purushottam Goel and Ylian Saint-Hilare*
*ISBN 978-1-934053-19-5*

Has your IT organization been hampered by the need for faster, more accurate asset management, reduced downtime with fewer deskside maintenance and repair visits, and improved malware prevention and response?

Would your business benefit from a solution for out-of-band manageability and security when the PC is in a low-power state or even powered off, the operating system is unresponsive, or software agents are disabled?

*Active Platform Management Demystified* shows how to gain these abilities, and more, by taking advantage of the hardware-assisted security and manageability features in notebook and desktop PCs equipped with Intel® vPro™ technology which is controlled by Intel® Active Management Technology (Intel® AMT). "Active Platform Management Demystified will become an important resource for anyone navigating state-of-the-art management technology." Winston Bumpus, Distributed Management Task Force president.

Arvind Kumar, Purushottam Goel and Ylian Saint-Hilare give a a complete description of how the features of Intel® AMT can be used to ease the burden of maintaining, managing and protecting PCs in both the Enterprise and Small Business environments. It has something for eveyone connected making computing more secure: "*Active Platform Management Demystified* provides a good balance between technology overview and implementation details, making it a great book for ISV product teams – including product managers, senior engineers, architects and support personnel." opines Max Sokolov of Symantec Corp.

Intel® AMT provides an access point for the latest management consoles from Microsoft*, Altiris*, Cisco*, LANDesk*, HP* and other Independent Software Vendors to allow IT practitioners to take advantage of Intel AMT features in the process of managing computers over a wired or corporate wireless network- or even outside the corporate firewall through a wired LAN connection. "Active Platform Management Demsitified thoroughly covers the concepts of Intel® vPro™ Technology and does a good job of explaining general system defense issues. Especially valuable is its description of the management of network filters used to identify and remedy potential threats." – Christoph Graham, Hewlett-Packard Technical Strategist

# *Dynamics of a Trusted Platform*
## *A Building Block Approach*
By David Grawrock
ISBN 978-1-934053-08-9

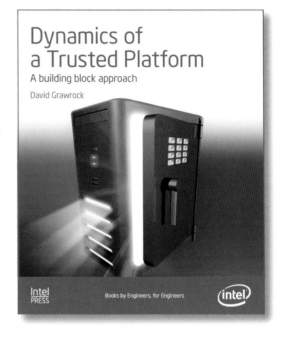

In Dynamics of a Trusted Platform David Grawrock has updated his highly popular Intel Safer Computing Initiative with new topics covering the latest developments in secure computing. The reader is introduced to the concept of Trusted Computing and the building block approach to designing security into PC platforms. The Intel® Trusted Execution Technology† (Intel® TXT) is one of those building blocks that can be used to create a trusted platform by integrating new security features and capabilities into the processor, chipset, and other platform components.

"The chapters on Anatomy of an Attack and System Protection present useful, practical information that will help familiarize a person with the impacts of protection (or lack thereof) of system components and resources. Treatment of the topic of measurement is particularly useful for system designers and programmers." - *Amy C Nelson, Dell, Inc*

"David finds analogies in everyday life to clearly explain many of the concepts in this book. I would highly recommended Dynamics of a Trusted Platform for researchers, architects, and designers who are serious about trusted computing." - *Dr. Sigrid Gürgens Fraunhofer Institute for Secure Information Technology (SIT)*

"The opportunity now exists to start building trusted systems, making this book very timely. It would be foolhardy to start without a thorough understanding of the concepts; and this is what Dynamics of a Trusted Platform gives you. The building blocks described here are certainly able to imbue the infrastructure with a higher level of trustworthiness, and we may all look forward to the many benefits flowing from that." - *Andrew Martin Director, Oxford University Software Engineering Centre*

# *Applied Virtualization Technology*
## *Usage Models for IT Professionals and Software Developers*

*By Sean Campbell and Michael Jeronimo*
*ISBN 978-0-976483-26-6*

Server and desktop virtualization is one of the more significant technologies to impact computing in the last few years, promising the benefits of infrastructure consolidation, lower costs, increased security, ease of management, and greater employee productivity.

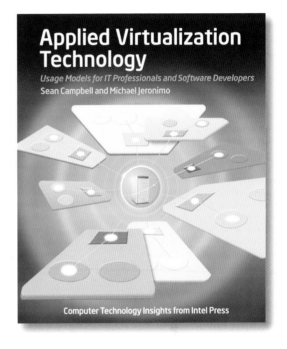

Using virtualization technology, one computer system can operate as multiple "virtual" systems. The convergence of affordable, powerful platforms and robust scalable virtualization solutions is spurring many technologists to examine the broad range of uses for virtualization. In addition, a set of processor and I/O enhancements to Intel server and client platforms, known as Intel® Virtualization Technology (Intel® VT), can further improve the performance and robustness of current software virtualization solutions.

This book takes a user-centered view and describes virtualization usage models for IT professionals, software developers, and software quality assurance staff. The book helps you plan the introduction of virtualization solutions into your environment and thereby reap the benefits of this emerging technology.

*Highlights include*

- The challenges of current virtualization solutions
- In-depth examination of three software-based virtualization products
- Usage models that enable greater IT agility and cost savings
- Usage models for enhancing software development and QA environments
- Maximizing utilization and increasing flexibility of computing resources
- Reaping the security benefits of computer virtualization
- Distribution and deployment strategies for virtualization solutions

# Energy Efficiency for Information Technology

*How to Reduce Power Consumption in Servers and Data Centers*
By David Grawrock
ISBN 978-1-934053-08-9

Minimizing power consumption is one of the primary technical challenges that today's IT organizations face. In Energy Efficiency for Information Technology, Lauri Minas and Brad Ellison point out, that the overall consumption of electrical power by data centers can be reduced by understanding the several sources of power consumption and minimizing each one. Drawing on their engineering experience within Intel Corporation and with the industry, they break down power consumption into its constituent parts and explain each in a bottom-up fashion. With energy consumption well defined, Minas and Ellison systematically provide guidance for minimizing each draw on electrical power.

Energy Efficiency for
Information Technology
How to Reduce Power Consumption in Servers and Data Centers

Lauri Minas and Brad Ellison

Intel
PRESS

Books by Engineers, for Engineers

(intel)

"Throughout my global travels, I hear increasing concern for the issues of power consumption by data centers, both due to the costs and also harm to the planet. *Energy Efficiency for Information Technology* addresses a critical issue for IT suppliers and consumers alike." Vernon Turner, Senior Vice President & General Manager, Enterprise Computing, Network, Consumer, and Infrastructure, IDC

"In *Energy Efficiency for Information Technology* Minas and Ellison underscore the magnitude of increases in power consumption, they systematically suggest ways to minimize consumption and provide checklists and assessments tables that are particularly useful to gather or summarize the right information for the planning. This is a multidimensional book that addresses a serious challenge to IT departments around the globe."
YY Chow, Managing Director, Systems and Securities Services, Mitsubishi-UFJ Securities

"*Energy Efficiency for Information Technology* is a remarkable compilation of cutting-edge technical knowledge for addressing the critical issue of power and cooling in data centers. It shows how your data center can compute more but cost less, while also reducing energy use and environmental impacts".
Jonathan Koomey, Ph.D., Project Scientist, Lawrence Berkeley National Laboratory

"Lauri Minas and Brad Ellison have written an important book that explains how diligent IT professionals can maximize the productivity of their data centers while minimizing power costs. These Intel engineers speak from experience and with authority. Anyone seriously interested in the greening of IT should read *Energy Efficiency for Information Technology*." Lorie Wigle, President, Climate Servers Computing Initiative.

# *Service Oriented Architecture Demystified*
## *A pragmatic approach to SOA for the IT executives*
*By Girish Juneja, Blake Dournaee, Joe Natoli, and Steve Birkel*
ISBN 978-1-934053-02-7

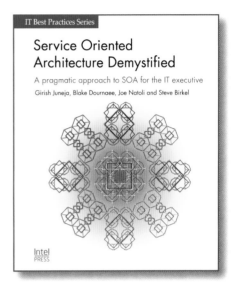

The authors of this definitive book on SOA debunk the myths and demonstrate through examples from different vertical industries how a "crawl, walk, run" approach to deployment of SOA in an IT environment can lead to a successful return on investment.

One popular argument states that SOA is not a technology per se, but that it stands alone and can be implemented using a wide range of technologies. The authors believe that this definition, while attractive and elegant, doesn't necessarily pass pragmatic muster.

*Service Oriented Architecture Demystified* describes both the technical and organizational impacts of adopting SOA and the pursuant challenges. The authors demonstrate through real life deployments why and how different industry sectors are adopting SOA, the challenges they face, the advantages they have realized, and how they have (or have not) addressed the issues emerging from their adoption of SOA. This book strikes a careful balance between describing SOA as an enabler of business processes and presenting SOA as a blueprint for the design of software systems in general. Throughout the book, the authors attempt to cater to both technical and organizational viewpoints, and show how both are very different in terms of why SOA is useful. The IT software architect sees SOA as a business process enabler and the CTO sees SOA as a technology trend with powerful paradigms for software development and software integration.

SOA can be characterized in terms of different vertical markets. For each such market, achieving SOA means something different and involves different transformational shifts. The vertical markets covered include healthcare, government, manufacturing, finance, and telecommunications. SOA considerations are quite different across these vertical markets, and in some cases, the required organizational shifts and technology shifts are highly divergent and context dependent.

Whether you are a CTO, CIO, IT manager, or IT architect, this book provides you with the means to analyze the readiness of your internal IT organization and with technologies to adopt a service oriented approach to IT.

# The Business Value of Virtual Service Oriented Grids

## Strategic Insights for Enterprise Decision Makers

By Enrique Castro-leon, Jackson He, Mark Chang and Parviz Peiravi

ISBN 978-1-934053-10-2

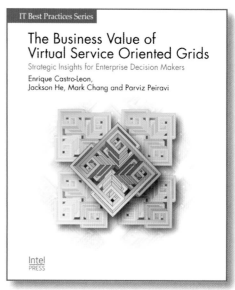

"In this book the authors track the trends, create new rules based on new realities, and establish new market models. With virtual service-oriented grids, the sky is the limit," writes Wei-jen Lee, a University of Texas – Arlington professor, about *The Business Value of Virtual Service Oriented Grids*, a new book published by Intel. The application of service-oriented architecture (SOA) for business will interest application developers looking for the latest advances in technology and ideas on how to utilize those advances to keep up in a global economy. *The Business Value of Virtual Service Oriented Grids* provides a framework that describes how the convergence of three well-known technologies are defining a new information technology model that will fundamentally change the way we do business. The first step, say the authors, is the development of new applications for the consumer market. However, even bigger is the development of new applications in a federated fashion using services modules called *servicelets*. These federated or composite applications can be built in a fraction of the time it takes to develop traditional applications. This new environment will lower the bar for applications development, opening opportunities for thousands of smaller players worldwide.

"We live in exponential times. . . . The economy is now thoroughly global. The Internet has replaced many of the middle layers of business, has enabled many to work from home or from a small company, and is revolutionizing the retail industries." writes Portland State University professor Gerald Sheble.

"The advent of SOA is going to impact information processing and computer services on a scale not previously envisioned." The speed-up in application development and integration will accelerate the deployment of IT capabilities, which in turn will have a consequential effect on the organization's business agility. Corporate decision makers will enjoy the ability to pick and choose among capital and operations expenses to suit their organization's business goals. The book describes the business trends within which this convergence is taking place and provides insight on how these changes can affect your business. It clearly explains the interplay between technology, architectural considerations, and standards with illustrative examples. Finally, the book tells you how your organization can benefit from *servicelets*, alerts you about integration pitfalls, and describes approaches for putting together your technology adoption strategy for building your virtual SOA environment using *servicelets*.

# About Intel Press

Intel Press is the authoritative source of timely, technical books
to help software and hardware developers speed up their development
process. We collaborate only with leading industry experts to deliver
reliable, first-to-market information about the latest
technologies, processes, and strategies.

Our products are planned with the help of many people in the developer
community and we encourage you to consider becoming a customer advisor.
If you would like to help us and gain additional advance insight to the latest
technologies, we encourage you to consider the Intel Press Customer
Advisor Program. You can register here:

## *www.intel.com/intelpress/register.htm*

For information about bulk orders or corporate sales, please send e-mail to:
**bulkbooksales@intel.com**

# Other Developer Resources from Intel

At these Web sites you can also find valuable technical information and
resources for developers:

| | |
|---|---|
| **www.intel.com/technology/rr** | Recommended reading list for books of interest to developers |
| **www.intel.com/technology/itj** | Intel Technology Journal |
| **developer.intel.com** | General information for developers |
| **www.intel.com/software** | content, tools, training, and the Intel Early Access Program for software developers |
| **www.intel.com/software/products** | Programming tools to help you develop high-performance applications |
| **www.intel.com/netcomms** | Solutions and resources for networking and communications |
| **www.intel.com/idf** | Worldwide technical conference, the Intel Developer Forum |

6177-0189-6736-7347

If serial number is missing, please send an
e-mail to Intel Press at intelpress@intel.com

---

**IMPORTANT**

You can access the companion Web site for this book on
the Internet at:

## www.intel.com/intelpress/qpied

Use the serial number located in the upper portion of
this page to register your book and access additional
material, including the Digital Edition of the book.